James C............

Terminal Chancer
Silver Seasons
Atlantic Salmon

Play happy

Boo

Illustrations by Danny Davidson

Featuring two collages by Christopher Aughton

1

First published in Great Britain in 2014 by The Guild of Reason

Copyright James Gilbraith 2014

Illustrations copyright Danny Davidson 2014

James Gilbraith asserts the moral right to be identified as the author of this work

A CIP Catalogue record for this book is available from the British Library

ISBN 978-0-9930771-0-4

Designed and typeset by Lee Walsh

CONDITIONS OF SALE

Acknowledgements

First and foremost I would like to thank all my wonderful family and friends for always being supportive and constructive. My amazing wife for allowing me to follow my passions so whole heartedly and completely, you are a patient and understanding woman.

I would also like to acknowledge the contribution from Danny Davidson both illustrating and spurring me on with his enthusiasm and praise for the book. Without Danny this book would still be an itch that needed scratching.

The very kind Francesca Robinson for doing all the proof reading and amendments.

I would also like to thank my many fishing friends who over the years have provided my life with so much colour and sunshine. You all know who you are.

I would like to express my gratitude to Craig Howard. His friendship is priceless.

This book is for my three loves, Anne Marie, Francis & Rose

Suggested Seasoning

Make Lists Do Something by Magic Arm
Arrow by The Heartless Bastards
Amateur Night at the Big Top by Shaun Ryder
The Three EP's by The Beta Band
These were the Earlies by The Earlies
Bummed by The Happy Mondays
Voodoo Chile by Jimmy Hendrix
Strictly Business by EPMD
Kenny Dennis EP by Serengeti
F Monday Orange February Venus Lunatic by Colourmusic
Astronomy for Dogs by The Aliens
Master of None by Jonnie Common
Sure Fire Ways to Sweeten The Mind By Sunstack Jones
Costa Blanca by The Liminanas
Thank God for Mental Illness by The Brian Jonestown Massacre
Diamond Mine by King Creosote and Jon Hopkins
Flick the V's by King Creosote
Love Is Simple by Akron/Family
The Very Best Of Maria Callas by Maria Callas
The Devil Went Down to Georgia by The Charlie Daniels Band
Just Loving You by Ruby Andrews

Chapter 1

Weights & Measures

"Come down Phil. Come on love, it's not that bad." Liz shouts coaxingly up at her husband as he stands on the ugly slanted rooftop of a featureless North West town hall. He's dressed in a brown jumper, chest waders and has a gye landing net slung across his back. What sets this scene apart from other suicide attempts is the large pink cardboard shrimp head mask, squarely sat on top of his shoulders. The day-glow disco pink shrimp head replica is the only splash of colour in this washed out grey landscape. Phil's face barely squeezes out of the oval cut out.

The shrimp head is an old relic from junior school; he had landed the less than glamorous role as a giant shrimp in the school's production of the Water Babies. Having been reduced to this role after a nasty incident at the last school nativity play - he had played the innkeeper and blew any chance of an acting career when he told Mary and Joseph that there was plenty of room in the inn and they should come in and make themselves comfortable. This untimely adlib in front of a packed school hall in front of the beaming gaze of sixty or so expectant parents....For many years the shrimp head had remained forgotten in the attic. Until today.

A small crowd has gathered at the base of the town centre building, curious to see what's happening on a normally docile Wednesday lunch time.

Two young police officers casually take photos of Phil on their smart phones and upload them to Facebook, while encouraging everyone to remain calm.

Phil is in his early 40s and is mournfully shouting the words, "eleven seasons, eleven seasons". He is openly sobbing.

Three men, jump out of a battered old green Ford Focus (Lamont, Andy, Mick) also in their 40s, arrive and stand alongside Liz. All three men look tired, untidy and carry the stale aroma of curry infused with tobacco.

"We came as soon as we heard, how long has he been there? He lost a nice fish then said he was going to get his head down in the car. It looks like he's come undone".

Liz : "He's been there for an hour. What the hell happened to him, I thought he was fishing with you lot?"

Phil is now sat down on the edge of the roof mumbling to himself in hushed tones while simultaneously shaking his head. He sees his friends and hangs his head.

Lamont calls up, "Phil it's not worth it, rain tonight, it'll be bang-on tomorrow, massive tides, there are still two thousand fish to come, and you know everything's a month late. Come down and let's talk about it....what did you lose that fish on, was it a Red Francis? What size hook? Where did he get that shrimp head from?"

Phil murmurs back with a weary tone...... "Nothing in

eleven seasons, nowt since my sixteen pounder in 1999."

The three men shoot knowing sideways glances at each other and Lamont again hesitantly shouts up using a reluctant yet patronising tone. "Mate it was more like fourteen…where did you get that shrimp head from?"

Phil lets out a loud sigh and continues to sob as he extends his landing net and swishes the air as though landing a fish, his antennae limply waves in the wind.

Liz shoots the men a glare that could vaporise them and hisses, "Morons, Phil is on a roof threatening to leap off, I don't think he's in the frame of mind for your bullshit. Are you mentally ill?" Lamont can neither confirm nor deny this question and offers Liz a shrug of his bony shoulders and adds meekly, "well it wasn't Liz, it was never sixteen pounds…Where did he get that shrimp head from he looks like Dali's phone."

Imagine the equine measurements of the face on any angler who fished for up to a hundred times a year, for eleven consecutive years and never caught anything, impotent as the male Giant Panda. This is a very real and present danger for a salmon fisherman. A horrible hellish nightmare that all too easily can become reality.

I once met a guy who hadn't caught anything for eleven seasons.... unbelievably he wasn't stark bollock naked, repeatedly screaming the number eleven from the rooftop of a recently clad municipal building, burning his rod licence and with a hand grenade duct taped to his face or for that matter; donning a giant pink cardboard shrimp head.

I had met him by chance; he had just arrived on the Lune two hours too late. I'll never forget his exasperated expression, his haunted traumatised eyes as he looked wistfully at the 3 fine fish on the bank and breathlessly explained, "I just couldn't get here any earlier, have they been through?...I've had the kids." This man was reduced to a slavering basket case, his mind worn down like a cheap tyre. I asked him how his season was going and he almost broke down as his tortured mind poured out its terrible secret, "the last one I had was eleven seasons ago". By the end of this terrifyingly dark story every person on that bank side had tears of fear and sorrow in their eyes. Even the casual dog walkers were choking up.....This broken picture could involve any one of us in the future and we all knew it. All it takes is a slight degree of change in any one of 1000 hellish uncontrollable variables.

My body is in the River Ribble stood in the steady current, casting my 15' fly rod. I am thinking of the poor man who I had met at the Lune some thirteen years ago and imagining the roof top scenario as a possible conclusion to his uneventful 12th season. It makes me smile as the morning wonder of spring sunshine energises me with a late flowering optimism and warm humour...... it's been a long winter without a cast but now I'm ready for the season on this wonderful river. I love fishing for Salmon so wholeheartedly that I can let its compelling nature wash over me completely.

The various bank side pedestrians look on as they trickle past. What they see is a man stood in the water looking like he's dancing to Chicago house music in some sort of late eighties illegal warehouse party. What is their perception of what I'm doing, what can they know? They don't see a man completely plugged into nature's circuit board. I feel the rhythm of the river pressing against my hips as I plot the course of the riverbed around me as a precise underwater radar grid reference; placing the position of boulders, holding spots and the varied depth of the river. I process the conditions and assess my chances; the air pressure around me has gently fluctuated while I wade slowly and thoughtfully through the pool. Insects hatch and take to the air intermittently. The bird song is vocally enhanced as the waveforms from my senses tune in to the world around me. ... So what can they know about our universe, a universe within touching distance of theirs but also so out of reach.....

Naturally there is a flip side to this as they gaze from the shrouded shoulders of the river bank. The average none angler's frame of reference for the outside of their house is the TV programme Countryfile. So I fit the description of the man in the river that featured for all of five minutes giving an irritating display of casting perfection by being just that; a man in a river seemingly trying to straighten a wonky piece of string. I'm not that man. I'm the man plugged into nature's circuit board with one hand clapping etc etc.

Actually those moments of beautiful nirvana are at best fleeting. As dog walkers and ramblers drift past like a creeping colourful gore-texed tide. I'm in the river with cold knees, one knotted shoulder bigger than the other, a sore back, one wet leg and my size too small wading boots slowly brutally crushing my toes and providing me with all the mobility of a fridge. Hung-over to the point that I feel as though I've been digested through a stray dogs bowel and creating time where there is none absconding from work. "I'm off to grab some toast and a brew," I had cheerfully chirped at 10.30am as I strolled out of the office and drove ten miles to the river for an hour. What can these people know as they wander down the river idly looking at the man in the river......

I once tried to explain test cricket to an American couple...they just couldn't understand that it can take 5 days and may still be a draw. Ditto – Salmon Fishing. Brothers and Sisters the Dali Lama would lose his rag and flip his lid if he had to explain the paradox of Salmon fishing and its various nuances to all the slack jawed none anglers out there. We all develop our coping strategies and roll them out when needed at social gatherings. I'm usually wheeled out like some loon with the repetitive conversation starter, "he's into fishing"... Look, it's not the normal peoples fault. It's ours. Once you are daft enough to outline the Salmon's life cycle then the average normal wants you to go away, stop talking, have a stroke, be flattened by a falling grand piano...anything, just stop.....It seems straight forward to us; river rises, river falls, salmon enter river. We fish for them...I always tail off. I can't commit to the conversation because it's utterly pointless. Words don't do it justice, all you are going to achieve is to confuse the normal person by mentioning any of the variables and convince them that you are wrong in someway...as a person, a head case - *I don't know what it is about him but he's just wrong.*

It's February on the River Ribble and I am fishing a beat I rarely take any notice of. Large spring tides have nicely coincided with just under two foot of water running off. There could be a vague shot at a Springer. A few Salmon anglers have also migrated back to the river, the searchers and seers dragged out of hibernation by restless optimism and compelled by our unpredictable mistress, Mother Nature. These few are usually the ones who know much but say little. Owning a skill set easily matching any expert surgeon and executing a cunning and guile worthy of any fidgety low level street pimp. They reduce the distance between themselves and the salmon simply by way of superior knowledge coupled with driving lust. By being out so early in the year at the perfect moment in time and space these few are elevated beyond those who merely talk a good game. On a river like the Ribble, sixty miles long with a spring run of only a few hundred fish, slowly dripping through from mid February to June they are the Captain Ahab's of anglers....almost tormented into fishing.

Walking back on to the club car park I see another

angler just arriving and automatically get the vibe that this man is an Ahab. Probably in his late fifties, his face like twenty layers of seasoned bark, in general good nick, not what I would consider sea-lice fresh but certainly not potted. So sternly quiet; almost sterile of any emotional giveaways. Seemingly not for him the joy of a warm spring day or the freedom from the economic grind; in fact no time for joy full stop, I'm suddenly transported to a scene from a Sergio Leone western, locked in a closed information duel of two sides. Lancashire has always been a popular destination for clouds and now they seemed to be jostling for the best viewing positions over this car park.

None flashy motor, rod and reel 15 – 20 years old, waders with at least three seasons wear complete with repairs, ancient, tatty Barbour wading jacket. He was stood steadily assembling his double handed fly-rod at the back of his car. A large scruffy frayed canvas holdall with two heavily spooled spinning reels poking out of the top. Obviously this was no purist, a man who fished the conditions. He rummaged around and produced a small well fingered fly box. I always warm to the potential theatre of the angler's car park. Friendly helpful anglers are plentiful but I find the clinically tight lipped are by far the best sport.

This was a man worth interviewing. My opening gambit was the universally accepted ice breaker, "river's in great nick." Silence. Crushing measured silence,

I begin to wonder if he is alive. I consider the middle ages technique of checking the dead by pricking them with a pin. I start fumbling around for a large hook. By this time Ahab decides to speak. "Aye it's bonny but it's too early yet – I'm just straightening a new line out to kill some time." I nod and agree that it's probably not worth the effort. No more information is exchanged although I know he's giving me the brush off – I start thinking about a recent scientific report about a strain of Ugandan Monkey, the males would tactically share their meat with other males in order to become a more effective hunting unit rather than share with the females in exchange for sexual favours. Ahab here, is certainly no Ugandan monkey, he's mortified that I am fishing this beat that he probably considers to be his own exclusive fishing – If this beat only has a couple of productive lies then the last thing he wants is somebody else getting to it before him – maybe I'm wrong but judging by the age and worn state of that "new" line, I'd bank on this beat being worth a revisit.

I'm getting my waders off quickly and stuffing my gear back into the boot with an eye on the clock, conscious that I should be back at work, especially as my employers still think that's exactly where I am. Just before I get in the car and say my goodbyes I ask Ahab how he went on last season. Ahab slung a well worn gye net over his shoulder and said "I missed most of last season because I had my hip done; I could only fish until mid September then I had to have my op. I asked them if they could delay it until November but they said no. Bloody NHS. I only managed 16...I'm waiting for a date for my knee to be done, I only hope they don't ask me in before winter comes."

Sixteen Ribble salmon and he missed the meat of the back end, incredible – all I could think of was Martin Sheene reading colonel Kurtz's military career file in the film Apocalypse Now. In my mind the jury had returned their verdict, Ahab was the real deal, you're not a proper Ribble salmon angler unless you have had a hip or knee replacement – you fish the river long enough and its inevitable. I wished him good luck and drove off making a mental note to give this beat some serious consideration – Ahab probably needed a long handled picker stick to put his pants on, this guy wasn't waring his joints out like a pestle grinding seeds in a mortar for nothing.

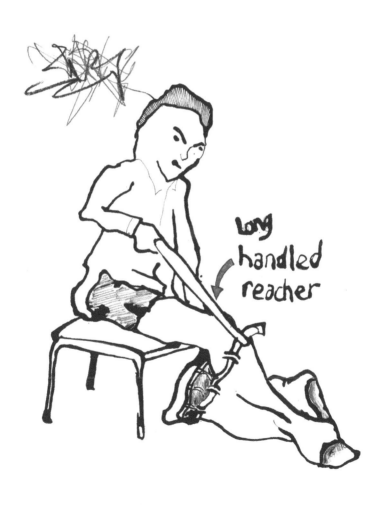

long handled reacher

My hamstring strain was a mere entry level injury, I could only aspire to accumulate enough bank side mileage to be on a bi-lateral waiting list – I wasn't fit to lace this blokes wading boots.

What this brief visit to the river told me all too clearly was that the season cycle had thankfully begun. I could step out of normal behaviour and engage with another invisible realm, one populated by people with only one thing on their mind – Atlantic salmon. Whether at work, a maternity ward, a birthday party, a meeting, in the car or plonked in front of the telly – physically they were present but mentally they were enjoying the last free frontier, a space that truly belonged to them – their minds and they were all just like me - absent.

Chapter 2

ABC Dee

Fire the arrow to kill the beast

Sometimes it's natural to cast off to new beginnings and pin fresh hopes to another form of sunshine. I am not one for sudden change. I need change to stalk me for years, gently creeping up without me noticing. It can't be a sharp sip or an icy plunge into the unknown. I often think about the first guy who cleverly hollowed out a log to create the first ever boat, desperate to leave the island and sail off into choppy unforeseen waters searching for a new adventure. I'd have been the bloke trying to talk him out of it as he dashes into the oncoming breakers. Patiently and optimistically, like a faithful springer spaniel I would watch the horizon for him to return, hopefully with the news that he shouldn't have bloody bothered in the first place. Gradually others would build their own boats and leave me behind until finally the penny drops and I conclude there's no alternative but to join them in the exodus.

Circumstance is the mother and father of invention; it's born from a muted frustration and simpering temptation. For four months I had slowly festered, stewing in my own juices through the feckless build up to the insanity that is Christmas and its assured anti-climax. I was dragged morose like a vulture stripped corpse though the mockingly grim piss-take of the month of January. Januarys is, to steal a phrase from Shaun Ryder, "like being beaten to death by clowns." Thankfully this flat line of a month eventually gives way to our new season on the River Ribble and restores a natural sense of purpose.

By this time I was ripe for reckless adventure; my encounter with Ahab had been my only brief outing due to a combination of insufficient time and incorrect weather. No matter how futile or the cost I had to get out somewhere. I had idly sifted through the irritatingly bountiful FishDee website, a site that appeared to be full of jolly bastards holding magnificent fish. Fishing propaganda is powerful bait, there's never a photograph of an angler without his quarry, crying while looking at his empty wallet. I had seen this at first hand while in Ireland in the mid 80's as part of a production crew for Hooked on Fishing. While filming a segment away from the Bream bashing international coarse action, we went to the Moy where the presenter got a double handed rod out and began to fish on low summer water. *One* whole hour passes and no fish... Not the best way for the Irish tourist board to advertise the silver lined fish filled rivers of Ireland. A car arrived; a salmon was taken out of the boot, hooked, filmed and landed. Ireland rejoiced. My fresh-faced teenage outlook instantly became savaged; my first wrinkle appeared in a subconscious protest and sneaked under my left eye.

So here I am reading the figures (while ignoring my subconscious telling me it's all propaganda) for the Dee in February with a frantic fist sized ball of anxiety bubbling in my chest, while desperately checking availability kicking myself for not hollowing out my boat sooner. It's time for me to join the masses and kiss the Ribble goodbye. I find the beat with the best February rod average...Christ! It's two hundred and forty quid a day!

Lower Crathes was the only beat that had two bookable rods left. Two hundred and forty pounds a day...each. Oh dear. I tried to find a sense of perspective – my Ford Focus only cost me eight hundred. I needed a second opinion – time to phone Lamont, my fishing companion of twenty-odd years. His fiscal tightness and love of bartering even the skinniest haggle is the thing of fable around our poker table. Lamont would talk some sense into me...

Lamont; a man who once compared himself to a meat samosa when trying to explain his complex, deep and mysterious personality. This dreadful analogy hit the mountain in flames as his bar room audience, who seemingly had escaped direct from an Edward Hopper painting, looked back with stagnant expressions as he explained his many layers. The young bar maid continued to empty out the slops and nodded as his jaw moved up and down. If ever there was a room that didn't need impressing; that was it. They would have been impressed that his shoes were on the right feet.

I could tell Lamont had been drinking when I phoned by the way he sounded... Cheerful. He was in his kitchen fighting with a dead goose that had been shot for dissent and given to him on a car park somewhere. He tried to explain the circumstances but I didn't have time to unravel his gleeful babel. I laid it on the line, gave it to him straight. This was *our* time – we had to do it now or we would die the ultimate death, one poisoned with regret. He paused mid goose, maybe he was asking it for an opinion, then I heard him sip something then hesitate, take a sharp intake of breath, then while exhaling he sighed, "oh fuck it, let's do it." So much for a sense of perspective, winter had obviously very nearly killed us.

Protocol (single people can skip this bit) dictates that for our migration to Aberdeen to proceed then we must pay the piper…be sanctioned and cleared for take-off by our spouses. I could carry on all piss and wind, telling you we just told them what was happening and that they had better get used to the idea… I started at begging and quickly descended into hysterical pleading... That's not what really happened. The joyful truth is that my wife could not wait to get me out of the way and put a temporary end to what she poetically calls static.

Static she claims is all she hears when I mention rivers, rainfall, tackle, books, methodology, clubs, ideology, idle gossip, surveys, data, analysis and anything at all of a fishing nature…

So we had done it, Lamont and I were on our way north. We had engineered a gap in time just for us - seventy two hours, free to clear off from under the shadow of responsibility. Not only that but we were on our way to a river that had its own catch figures – it actually had salmon, plural, in it.

Our one day's expensive fishing wasn't the best planned event in the world but we didn't care. The invention of the running with the bulls in Pamplona must have been initiated by the same school of gung-ho thought process. Pillion passengers in motorcycle sidecar racing use the term - brain out, brick in. It had been time to reduce thinking and get running. So what if we needed a day to travel two hundred and sixty miles, an overnight stay, fish all day until they threw us off, another overnight stay then drive home arriving home just in time for tea – three days for one days fishing.

I picked Lamont from his walled, astro-turfed compound at 8am; I could see that he was lit and ready. Obviously he had packed two salmon rods, a spinning rod and a trout rod – was he planning on fishing from a moving vehicle on the M6? Our schedule seemed fairly water tight but he insisted that we may get chance to fish the Eden on the way up. Apparently the trout rod was 'just in case'.

Topics of conversation in the car included:

1. Lamont's patented copyrighted trademarked salmon skull clear resin wader stick business – a highly complex environmental plan involving the collection of salmon skulls from the redds and encasing them for eternity in a clear epoxy resin. We figured that it had many different applications but mainly on top of wading sticks.

Paper weights were an extinct relic of the past and we weren't prepared to travel that road, we were too street for that. Neither of us owned a wading stick and we put this down to being unable to purchase one with a resin salmon skull on it. Granted, we had no prior knowledge of how many bones made up a salmon skull – at this point the facts were redundant. Our theoretical baskets would be over flowing with skulls plucked from our abundant Ribble redds and we would be backing the van up to unload them direct into the resin factory. At this point in the conversation Lamont leaned in to me and reminded me that it was his idea.

This debate and eventual wrangling for stock options took us to Penrith – we stopped and had a full English breakfast; it's the holiday law.

2. What would you do if you caught the record – if in the unlikely event; you managed to catch an Atlantic salmon so huge that it beat Miss Ballantines 64lb record fish?

I knew the answer to this:

1. Catch it
2. Kill it
2a. Kill it again
3. Stuff it
4. Ask expert taxidermist to make it as silver as possible
5. Instruct expert taxidermist to add small stuffed sea lice
6. Have expert engraver inscribe the brass plaque with the legend: *Heroically caught during an epic duel on 8lb line, single handed 8ft rod and a barbless size 16 variant*
7. Mounted in a mahogany bow fronted case of the highest quality and placed over my fire place

8. On my own death have my loving and understanding wife; follow my final instructions to have me stuffed complete with satisfied/smug look on my face, stood and dressed in my waders and fishing gear, arm outstretched and pointing

9. Placed in the corner of the lounge pointing at my record capture

10. Ensure that my will is amended so that both of us are never parted and that we may be donated to the national history museum, only if they give us our own wing

Lamont agreed that the fish was never going to go back, it wouldn't be a record unless it died. It would be the gift that kept giving – guest tickets to world famous beats and immortality – Lamont was quick to tell me that the first thing he would do was get himself an agent. When fame came knocking he wanted a professional, I think the exact quote was, "I couldn't afford to take advice from a joker like you, in cases like this you need a ruthless specialist, totally fluent in the language of these multimedia fucktards." In his head he was already on the after dinner speech and chat show circuit raking up £15k an hour retelling the greatly embellished tale of capture. Yes he mused, to return a fish like that would be a crime to ourselves and our families, but mainly ourselves. He also warmed to the notion of being stuffed when he was dead, preferring instead to loom in a vertical elongated state, arms aloft and outstretched complete with nunchucks and contorted sneering expression in the marital bedroom, overseeing Mrs Lamont while she finished her coco and Sudoku instead of the window cleaner.

3. Recession proof wood pigeons:

It had occurred to Lamont that the only things doing well for themselves during the current fiscal climate were the humble, flexible and sturdy wood pigeon. He had made this observation journeying through southern Scotland. The logic was that the wood pigeon was clever enough to keep it simple. Even with a brain the size of a micro-dot, they had ignored the gloomy economic outlook and continued to maintain by using the basics; eat, sleep, reproduce and be happy with one home. We wondered how long it would take the government to place some sort of penalty or tax on their robust business model – a let's tax the pigeons bill. The opposition would no doubt use the bird as a success story to be shared and adapted into daily life.

Indeed it was difficult to find a flaw in his thinking – they had continued to buck the trend.

When we had booked our little trip I had one slight problem, my waders were away being resuscitated. For a new pair of waders the River Ribble is a death sentence, from the moment you have unpacked them from the box that contained them, the mournful trumpets of a Gulag orchestra sound in recognition of their steady decline, a slow and punishing death sentence as gruelling as a baking Louisiana chain gang or a brutal freezing Gulag Archipelago labour camp. Within one year they will most certainly be dead, looking like they have been savagely attacked by some frenzied predator – face a firing squad with them on – they will do less damage. Obviously I'm talking about wearing them frequently within a season but the simple action of taking them off 100 times in a year could be enough to banjax most waders, never mind the ferocious terrain that awaits you. Every single plant, animal, fence, stile, gate, stone, boulder, aggregate, machine, industrial compound, fertiliser, hedge and tree destroy or contribute to the wear of these delicate essential garments. Even the action of just walking around in them wears out the seams as your legs brush together. So I have, after some extensive experience, decided that all makes, styles and fabrics are fucked after a year so there is no point buying something expensive. Now my waders get sent to a Scottish wader hospital for the severely traumatised.

Diver Dave's Wader Repair in Aberdeen (DDWR) – 50 quid to repair and reseal every hole and every seam – it's a steal. That's where my waders were, DDWR in Aberdeen, I wasn't much bothered about the turnaround time when I sent them after the last lot of February rain. I had decided that with a new season I deserved to be dry for at least a short time. With the trip booked I had fretted that they may not be ready. After a brief phone call I was told that they were done and that I could collect them direct.

DDWR restored our faith in humanity – what three men in monogrammed boiler suits could do with an ironing board, laptop, washing line, industrial air hose and a truck load of aquaseal, made our hearts soar. These three noble men had found a business as recession proof as the humble wood pigeon. All I will divulge is that my waders were repaired and had been in the hands of a true craftsman – the Willy Wonka of Waders, if you will.

We arrived at the Douglas Arms, Banchory at 4pm and hit the bar for a holiday pint. Lamont was skittish about the safety of our tackle in the car, (even though I had neatly twerked the arse end up to a brick wall to make access to the boot impossible), so we brought every bit into our hotel room. The nice tidy twin room now looked like a burgled tackle shop. We planned a night of equipment maintenance to ensure nothing was left to chance – lines cleaned, flies fluffed, gluing braided loops and general repairs to other bits and bobs all needed to be completed. As a result it looked like the tide had gone out and left a dirty signature. Lamont produced his clockwork fly vice and an ugly tin full of bird and animal parts that would have done any Lassa witch doctor proud. We had been there thirty minutes and we had already decided that under no circumstances should any of the hotel staff be allowed admittance. We hadn't exactly soaked the room's rug in ether but the room was in a state of shock. We returned to the bar, had a couple of pints and went for a mooch into town via the local Orvis shop.

Buoyed by our 'on holiday' status and with having nothing difficult or demanding to do, we entered the opulent and beautiful Orvis shop which was full of things we couldn't afford as we had blown all our money on a day's fishing. When Lamont had finished his grilling of the helpful shop assistant; about what seemed to me ultra specific current conditions and catch reports, we felt obliged to buy some flies that were local favourites. We bought two each. Orvis could shut the shop early and break out the party hats.

After two more pubs, bromance was in the air as we booked into a small Italian restaurant that was right next door to our digs. Lamont had thought it necessary to inform the waiter that we were both married – when the waiter smiled and nodded (being polite) Lamont

quickly amended his statement with "not to each other…
to women." After two main courses and a bottle of house
red we decided to walk around the back of the pub and
have a joint – since the smoking ban, all smokers are
now outcasts. You can usually see them huddled outside
in clusters like scabies or prisoners in the exercise yard,
shuffling around shoegazing. All smoking zones are
situated in the bleakest areas, as enticing as a nuclear
winter. It has levelled the playing field though for those
of us who are the occasional pot smoker. And so we found
ourselves glamorously behind the hotel, by the bins, in
the drizzle – briefly being outlaws, having a joint and
laughing at our good fortune to be where we were at that
moment in time and space.

We returned to our hotel room armed with hazy
optimism, a bottle of wine, chocolate and crisps. Lamont
had said that he had a surprise for me. Obviously I was
concerned. Out of his bag he produced, Topher Browne's
Atlantic Salmon Magic – a book that had cost one hundred
pounds. A Christmas present from Mrs Lamont, its glossy
contents were potent stuff on the eve of our big day. We sat
on our twin beds amongst our tackle nest, reading passages
aloud and laughing at the sheer size of contrast. The books
exotica are a billion miles away from our fishing on the
Ribble. We put on the DVD that accompanies the book
while we attended to our tackle repairs and reasoned that
Topher's fishing advice tended to be most effective on
rivers containing a run of only about two million fish.

During this time we had realised that we had no corkscrew for the wine – this was extremely distressing. Neither of us wanted to go downstairs and ask for one, we felt it would have been far too risky. Luckily I had seen a clip of a wine bottle being uncorked with a man's shoe on youtube. Cautiously over the bath I held the bottle by the neck upside down – with Lamont's size 11 boot in my other hand ready to strike the base of the bottle square on. I took a firm grip of both and struck the bottle at slow to medium pace, eyes shut and fearing the worst...BANG -the cork moved – halleluiah! It sounded like I was firing a small calibre hand gun in a small Scottish bathroom but it was working. Lamont quickly turned the TV up to drown out the sound of the gunshots. With a new vigour I quickly turned up the heat and came at it like Michael Holding bowling at Tony - make them grovel Greig. Voila, the cork came out with the bottle intact. To us the successful uncorking of the wine was a sign and a symbol that we could overcome adversity by the strength of our own guile. Lamont genuinely thought it was a miracle. After the DVD and another covert trip to the bins we hit the hay eager for the Dee.

After a massive early morning breakfast which thankfully had the effect of sedating Lamont from his fidgety stage nerves – he had never fished with a gillie and he was anxious not to make a fool of himself.

Lamont had previous when it came to interactions with others in seemingly ordinary transactions.

1. Barred for life from a local aquatic shop when returning three fish which had died within five minutes after being released into his stagnating toxic aquarium.

2. Police called when returning a charger for a phone at our local branch of Comet – after a dispute with a "cocky" store manager.

3. Banned from a local smoke house when he argued that they had under weighed a salmon he had left for smoking – "where's the rest of it?"

Today however, he was eager to please.

We arrived at the fishing hut and were warmly greeted by the head gillie Robert Harper and his fellow gillie Chaz. I felt that my modest T registered Ford Focus must have told them all they needed to know about us. I don't think we were their usual clients and when I informed them of our own Ribble catch per visit ratios they both kind of grimaced. Robert had been on this beat over twenty years, so he had seen it all at least twice before. I'm not sure he could relate to our plight as determined Ribble fishers although I'm sure he could empathise that we were both keen. Robert and Chaz started to unload the car of our nets and wading boots so they could disinfect them. If the car hadn't got the point across about where our priority's lay then surely our waders and tackle certainly did – we may not have been Ahabs but both of us considered ourselves seasoned – we wanted these two complete strangers, on this the most expensive days fishing we had ever had, to like us. As proud, warm humoured Lancastrians we had a national stereotype and reputation to up-hold, of grin and bare it *-arte et labore* - hard fishers who happily hardly caught fuck-all.

It's safe to say that Lamont and I both felt awkward that somebody else was stringing up for us – it felt completely alien to us and we didn't know what to do, so in ten minutes flat we nervously gave them a capsule insight of the last twenty odd years on the Ribble. Robert kindly saved us from ourselves and suggested we both go inside the cabin for a brew. By now we had plenty of chance to gaze at the magnificent river in front of us. The height was, according to Robert "bang on." This set our pulses racing with anticipation. It was a bracingly cold, clear, fine day with not even a seductive whisper of wind. For a booked in advance days fishing we could not have landed luckier.

It was finally time to turn our talents to the river.

> Tackle:
> I was using my three piece Hardy Demon 15ft rod, a Greys Xflite reel with an oldish wet cell two slow sinking line and an Airflow 5ft fast sink tip with a Dee Monkey at the point of sale.

Lamont's tackle:

Lamont had treated himself for the first time in twenty years and he had gone big. After much indecision, discussion and a lengthy search for justification, he had bought a Loop Cross S1 14ft coupled with a Loop Classic 811 reel – and several Rio lines and tips – I can't tell you what fly he was using because he wouldn't show me.

We jumped into a 4x4 and were taken down to the lower beat for the morning. Lamont would fish two hundred metres above me. Chaz and I waded across the river into the mid current and he directed me on where to shoot. He watched me cast for a short while and when he was confident that I wasn't a complete knob or that I wasn't going to drown he left and went back to Lamont.

I was so happy to be there in that river riding the tantalising wave of optimism that came with every single cast. It really did feel very special, emotional and exciting. Winter was all around us and the snow had kissed every hill top and framed the river beautifully. I was going to appreciate every minute because I knew all too well that I was punching massively above my fiscal weight.

It had been a long journey to get here and I'm not talking about the car ride up the M6. Whether aged eleven watching my delicate Indian reed float bob between the lily pads on the Lily pond in Witton park, Blackburn, hoping for a tench or gudgeon bashing on the Leeds and

Liverpool canal every weekend with all my mates - I was always compelled by the what if nature of fishing. Each cast an absorbing individual case study of hope. So now, aged 44 and stood in the Dee, I remembered my boyhood fishing trips with my friends and thought about some of my angling friends who had died far too young. That first half an hour alone in the river was quite emotional for me, feelings I hadn't planned on encountering came to the surface – I fished on and the line tightening soon restored my factory settings.

As I returned the Kelt I could see Lamont over at the other side quite animated struggling to assert his casting technique on the river. His head bowed looking down at his reel and tugging at the line. Chaz watched five or six more attempts and decided to intervene. Now Chaz was casting hopelessly and muttering to Lamont. Meanwhile I am back in the water and into another kelt that is landed and returned with minimum fuss but tinted with a touch of disappointment that the take hadn't been from a springer. I look back up stream and see Lamont's new reel coming off and Chaz's spare reel going on. Now the line is going out fine and both men look pleased.

We moved down further to a couple more spots – Chaz expertly moved the pair of us down the beat ensuring we covered plenty of water. He was more than perplexed by Lamont's reel, "I cannee understand it, that line woodnee cast," he shook his head while explaining that he had to lend Lamont his own reel and line. Lamont had also now returned two kelts, so was fishing with our greatest weapon – confidence. But I knew that inside his cranium there would be an element of turmoil as he interrogated himself over the failure of his new kit.

By lunch time we had caught six kelts between us and reluctantly we were forced to have an hour in the cabin for lunch. Lamont walked me though his line and casting theories but he was still no closer to unravelling the mystery, he would examine the reel and line back in the privacy of our hotel room – I could tell he had fallen out with them and the last thing he wanted was the incident pursued and dissecting publicly during lunch with the other two unknown guests and the gillies.

Lunch over and we are whisked up to the top end. I connect with something very solid and heavy. Chaz is behind me saying this looks like it could be yer springer. It took line and stole deep for a few minutes hoodwinking my heart and head but was all too soon beaten and was now cradled in Chaz's net, with my view partially obscured he now announced that it was a kelt of about 15lbs. For the final two hours we fished the bridge pool. I had nothing more to declare other than a bastardly brief on off, on my second run through the bridge pool following Lamont. With the February sun dropping in the sky we called it quits at 5.45pm and drove back to the hut in my car. The day hadn't been a masterpiece like the Dave Pearson career defining painting, Byzantium or an album as fantastic as The Three EP's by The Beta Band, but maybe that was a good thing – we still had those monuments to aspire to.

Lamont and I took some photos of each other with broad grins outside the cabin almost forgetting how cold we were, thanked Robert for a fabulous day and awkwardly left forty quid on the cabin table and drove off into the sunset back to the boozer for a pint, a warm and debrief.

After a few pints we got out Lamont's reel – it would appear that in his semi lushed up state the night before – Lamont had inadvertently attached another intermediate head to his already intermediate head – doubling the length of his intermediate head – to this he then cunningly attached a sinking head and tip. Solving the mystery of why his finely tuned instrument had bucked and lunged when handled in his hour of need. What happened next was the cherry on top – Lamont with reel in hand turned to me and declared, "The fault, dear Brutus, is not in our stars, but in ourselves, that we are underlings." Lamont, the meat samosa; hand in hand with big Billy Shakespeare - like us and the Ribble hand in glove with the Aberdeenshire Dee. Perfect timing is a thing of beauty – a joy forever.

Naturally our debrief turned us into quasi philosophers; declaring all the classic clichés that we couldn't have done anymore, we had caught it right – it was a brilliant day anyway etc but what really made the day superb was the fact that both of us had failed to catch a springer. That morning over breakfast we had both sounded like Mahatma Gandhi stating the opposite, and repeating the sporting mantra "as long as one of us catches one." But inside, we both knew the truth... two hundred and sixty miles is a long long drive home with a smug cunt sat next to you.

Chapter 3

Turning Pro-Biotic

My insight into the day in the life of a world famous salmon river at the Dee had left me slightly tarnished; my eyes had seen the glory. The Ribble now had a kind of dilapidated Detroit lustre. I had a sense of loss and of reality – I was lucky enough to have a salmon river on my own doorstep but it remains a river in terms of prominence at least, anonymous and fairly low down on the hit parade.

I wasn't divorcing the Ribble but I felt that we both needed a break; some time to think and reflect about what we both needed and wanted from our relationship. Maybe we had taken each other for granted. I had strayed but was I responsible? Or was it natural, after all I had certain needs. I had given myself a taste that life could be different and now I schemed how I could attach myself like pro-biotic bacteria to the moneyed elite and fall head-first between the firm, fertile thighs of a new mistress. All it had taken was for the Dee to show me a flash of inner thigh and my head had been turned.

I had drifted gently into my mid-forties realising that my tastes have gradually changed. It used to be a simple case of letting the dog see the rabbit and then letting the dog run. Since becoming a resolutely married family man, my top shelf material has become just as exotic and even more unrealistic. During the calm stolen moments of time and space within the sanctuary of my bathroom, I can indulge my dirty shame, while scenes, not unlike the siege of Stalingrad erupt across the rest of the house, I can remain momentarily unreachable while out of the main capsule on an exploratory space walk through the pages of my favourite literature.

For twenty precious minutes a day I can lock the door and open the ultimate gentleman's handbook and excitedly thumb through the well worn pages of Fred Buller's doomsday book of giant salmon. OOOOhhhh baby...My oh my, it should come with a health warning. How I long to be dragged, gillie, boat and all, heart pumping like a national runner through two turbulent pools of the Alta backwards attached to a silver rocket weighing fifty plus pounds. If there was an adult chat number to hear it being read in breathless and sultry tones I'd be ringing... "It's absolutely massive, I've just seen its head,"… Christ, I can't take it...

Having read this book continually for two years, one thing becomes all too apparent. The Ribble isn't the Alta...I aspire to the Alta like a kid wants to be an astronaut*, indeed I may have more chance of space travel in my bathroom than getting to grips with the suggestively fertile banks of this tease of a river.

The common theme in most salmon fishing literature is this; many of the anglers featured have names just like

I had, except their names were prefixed by words like, Sir, Major, Colonel, Duke, Earl, General, Lieutenant, Admiral, Lord, Captain and Baron. Why had these dudes caught all the fish on all those world famous beats? It was high time I dedicated some time to research and painstaking planning. I would either have to become nouveau riche or quickly shin up the honours list and get myself a title worth having. Or maybe there was another less arduous route...

The closest I came to owning a recognised prefix was when I had ordered a jumper from Orvis – on the address menu, the website gives you a title option on the name drop down. Who wouldn't pimp up their name? I chose to be a Professor – a universally respected title, oozing knowledge, expertise, patience, dedication and beards. I had a beard but lacked the rest. So once my jumper arrived, addressed to Professor Boo Gilbraith, it was official. It was already working; the postman actually spoke to me – "a parcel for you Professor." Using my third eye I could clearly make out my hand creeping deep inside a Fortnum and Mason hamper fettling an 'A list' pork pie, while led out bank side, entertaining my new companions with my gentle wit and engaging charm, "ah yes, the Ribble really is a terrible river, it's as empty as a fitters head."... I had begun my social climb.

No such daydreams for the Duke of Roxurghe it would seem. Generations of his family's exceptional Alta angling exploits make up a good half of the book's

stella content…Yes; somehow I've got to get close to the duke as his firm have the Alta watertight. Having looked at the Duke's form on Wikipedia it's glaringly apparent that we swim in two very different pools, his being vast, influential, deep and exotic. Mine a limited festering puddle of toxic freaks… I'm not likely to bump into him falling out of my local, the New Inn, Clitheroe, the local car boot sale or zipping round Aldi. I'm struggling to make Ascot or the next worshipful company of fishmongers meeting. I can't rely on my comprehensive school tie network as surprisingly it seems Eton still has the edge when it comes to the word exclusive.

Maybe I could do him a favour; historically Dukes and Barons are partial to a good favour…a quick, quiet murder or well-timed double cross could go a long way… I'm limited to how far my favour could extend for a shot at the Alta, maybe I could volunteer for the DOR Alta work party or work out a Ribble exchange ticket. I've mentioned "a favour for the duke" to the wife and she knows how much it would mean to me. Usually she's a game old filly (I don't know why I used that term – its bloody awful, maybe subconsciously I'm trying to get into the aristocracy's mindset?), but on this occasion the stubborn brute has drawn a line, so that shapely avenue has been firmly closed. I've no intention of becoming the next Sir William Walworth as that kind of behaviour has become more risky these days due to the inconvenient onset of digital media. Murderous exploits of London Mayors would be straight on youtube and therefore surely unspinnable. Who knows what skulduggery has gone un-detected in the name of exclusive fishing rights or maybe it was all done for mutual benefit and gratification... who knows, certainly not me.

According to Maslow

Are we really that different, the Duke and I? Surely we could get along just for a week or so the two of us in ten miles of dramatic beauty of the Altaelva wilderness. After all, we both share the same simple physiological needs, breathing, food, water, large salmon, sleep and sex. Granted not all at once, but let's start tenderly on common ground. Maslow then kindly allows us up his pyramid to safety. Staying healthy, contemplating morality, being secure…secure in our humble homes, or in the Dukes case, multiple homes, massive castle and private estate. Our level of comfort gained from security is obviously subjective. Climbing further into the thin air of Maslow's theory we elevate to love, belonging and esteem. This is clearly aimed at *us*, brothers in arms, angling unified by our universal mentality and common goal. It can't possibly be interpreted in any other way. Sitting at the top of the all singing and dancing, one hand clapping pyramid is the neon signed Self-actualisation of morality, creativity, spontaneity, problem solving, lack of prejudice and acceptance.

Where better to realise this accent to nirvana than the banks of the Alta with a complete stranger…

Maybe I should drop him an email and outline my aims and objectives and pass on my credentials.

This should do the trick.

Aloha

Having read Fred Buller's fantastic book, 'The Doomesday Book of Giant Salmon' and fully fallen under its spell, I now have an itch named the Alta that urgently needs scratching like giant hogweed in my eyes. How does one go about getting on this amazing river? I am available to leave my wife, family and job at extremely short notice if a place becomes available.

I can assure you that I am discreet, affable and considered a fun guy.

Availability

I've had a quick flick though the wall calendar and apart from a 65th birthday party at the Cricket Club on the 7th and a wedding on the 21st of July, I can declare myself fully available and ready to travel at the drop of an email to my inbox. In the event of an unforeseen overlap in my almost socially redundant calendar and our fishing trip; fear not... I always carry my sudden illness card, "pleurisy has flared up, or my gout's creasing me." Either of these are usually ample for a cancelation, rarely have I had to use both barrels at once.

Don't worry about flights etc. Don't trouble yourself, I will stand those. As a thank you I can guarantee the finest wines known to Aldi or Lidl.

Any information will be gratefully accepted.

Regards, Prof Boo Gilbraith

One week later I received alarming news from my new chums.

Dear Prof Boo

With regards to your email of 8th June, I am afraid the Duke and his family only fish the River Alta they, unfortunately, do not own it so we are unable to offer any fishing there. I would suggest that you contact Visit Norway which is the official tourist board for Norway. I have had a quick look and their website does provide information including contact details for the River Alta.

Yours sincerely, Kelly

Oh well it was worth a punt –

*kids don't really want to be astronauts anymore. They want to be virtual...

Chapter 4

One of us is dead

The Earlies

May

The River Intelligence Services on the internet had confirmed my darkest fears; the river was receding and clearing to a near perfect fishing height. Exciting times illuminated by the prospect of a pitch perfect day on the river. There was one ugly problem – I was marooned inside my workplace, peering through our office windows at the panoramic slate grey Blackburn skyline. Light rain slid down the windows as I looked out over at a bleak Poundstretcher super store, parallel to a high in cholesterol, congested, angry main road which was under the shadow of one of the most bankrupt lobotomised areas of Blackburn. Behind me was a PC gleefully displaying the gateway to another world not that far away - tide times and the current height of the Ribble, shown in the form of a beautiful graph. I turned again and looked at the living Hieronymus Bosch outside, and then I caught my own reflection and mumbled out loud "one of us is dead." Listening to this song by The Earlies is a weekly totem for me to get my shuffle on and focus. Now my own reflection was mocking me – we looked like we both needed to fish. Should I just bang on the windows and shout – help! Maybe not, help would probably arrive in the shape of a surly roided-up youth being towed by a Josef Mengele crossed pit bull named Rizzla. What made it worse was the fact that I knew full well that a number of rods would be out – including Lamont.

He would be moving in glorious Technicolor being powered by psychedelic vibrations – roaring Hammond and fuzzed guitar chords from the Velvet Underground, Brian Jones Town Massacre or even the Liminanas from France, driving down the country roads in his work dodging salmon space capsule, fist punching, volume revved and high on hope - the shitheal. My work-life balance was rammed head first down a festival crapper, choking on a turd.

This situation would have been a formality had it not been for our rabid human resources department. Phoning in sick or sliding out of the cracker factory for four hours and then calmly slithering back in without detection was the norm for this kind of scenario – they had reeled me in the week before with the disarming but completely fake "is everything all right, we just want to make sure that you are ok as you have reached a trigger point of instances of absence…" It wasn't easy to quell the fury within every bone but I couldn't expose myself – I had to think of the long game, and of salmon... I had a quick mental check of my posture - that I didn't give any tell tale visual clues, made sure nothing was crossed or folded and responded in a casual manner. I thought of John Le

Mesurier, smiled and dove in, "that's frightfully kind of you to be concerned about my wellbeing but there really is nothing wrong other than the odd unfriendly stomach bugs and awful viruses," (kill them with kindness – the miserable fucksticks). So I sat politely and listened to the rules of their game: I had taken the grand total of eight sick days off in the year - one instance of absence could be up to six months off but it only counts as one. Most of my sick days were single days off around the fat months of Sept – Oct when the river dropped right – counted by HR as individual instances of absence – six being the trigger for a back to work interview. I had hoped that a panel of drab Dickensian bean counting HR shrews would have ambushed me with a massive file of incriminating evidence, CCTV footage of me breaking out of work and finally confronting and exposing my activities with a colour coded wall projected graph that clearly showed my September/October fourteen year absence spike. It was a mild disappointment that my skiving exploits remained unsung.

This book could end up being Hari-Kari, a thirty thousand word self mugging resignation letter…

In theory I could take Tuesday to Friday off five times in a twelve month period and never get flagged. This information was handy for the future but I would remain on what was described as a watch list for six months just in case there was anything wrong in my personal life that they could *help* out with. The whole process was loathsome and contemptible. I resented being a human resource and thought of in the same context as a broken stapler or bent paper clip but now at least I could beat them with their own shitty stick. Did these HR velvet thugs not know I was married to an exclusive competition?... The Salmon Weasel doesn't win itself, I didn't like my head being over the parapet in plain sight for these battery hens to take pot shots. I needed to consolidate my position, dissolve into the background - keep my head down for six months then coast through September and October being able to hit the river for three or four days at a time. I can't wait until I'm having my hips and knees replaced and I've become more machine than man – THEN HR will know what an instance of absence truly is. Like arthritis, water always finds the cracks.

The beauty of contest can be framed perfectly by the trophy presented at the end of an enduring classic encounter. We all compete on a daily basis and collect occasional kudos along with a selection of metaphorical trinkets and trophies that help give us some meaning while gently massaging our egos. Our lists probably include:

Rods, reels, clubs, friends, stories, partners, houses, jobs (careers in some extreme cases) wrinkles, children, cars, clothes, jewellery, holidays, books, records...to name a few.

I'm describing the contest...hopefully the long game of life which offers our rewards both gracefully and gradually, usually delivered along the sometimes chaotic bumpy road of love and loss.

Some of my favourite trophies bear no resemblance to the effort, skill, strain and struggle that makes the trophy worth winning in the first place.

The yellow jersey – after a 3000 mile murderous bike race you get a yellow polyester top.

The Ashes – after up to 25 days of cricket on 5 different grounds you get a 3 inch urn full of sand.

Olympic gold – After four years of training, qualifying and beating a field of thousands you get a gold medal made of 92% silver.

Boxing – nose, speech, eyes and brain all in tatters... you receive a giant belt.

Poultry contest Great Yorkshire show - £12 to get in, £10 to enter each bird, three months of obsessive secretive micro prep – intensive breeding programmes, hand rearing – shampooing and bathing in fairy liquid (pimped plumage shine) 1st prise = £10, 2nd prise £8, 3rd = £4. My next door neighbour had won twenty two quid from his three plucky show birds. He was happy with his rosettes, even though he did lament his petrol bill. This is the difference between professionals and gnarly hobbyist.

And the award goes to... oh, well done darling.

Then there are the prizes in recognition of your talent and hard work; there is a growing market for industry awards. You could get one for having a face – especially if that face had paid two thousand pounds for a table to attend the ceremony… Many of these marketing pop-up ideas are derived from the Oscar, the glittering film award that sets the tone in the entertainment industry. If you're not lucky enough to get an Oscar then you may get a BAFTA, this is like expecting steak and getting a pot noodle compared with the stars and striped might of the Oscar.

For the great humanitarians, you could bag The Nobel Peace Prize. Writers may get a Booker or a journalist could get the Pulitzer Prize. All guaranteed gateways to instant Western World recognition...

So where does all this leave us...the humble salmon angler?

Contest

1. Competition to find the best: an organised competition

for a prize or title, especially one in which the entrants appear or demonstrate their skills individually.

The brass plaque simply reads: Salmon Weasel

Salmon Weasel annually awarded for: Catching an Atlantic Salmon by being on the river when you really should be somewhere else. i.e. at work, at home, doing shopping, D.I.Y (it means do it yourself... it doesn't mean ask me) with the kids...some other shit.

These are the simple, plain T&C's of the Salmon Weasel. To cut through time and catch a fish when everybody thinks you're being compliant and hog tied to burdensome responsibility. The award ceremony takes place at the Bay Horse on the first Saturday of November when the nominations have been sifted through and ratified. The winner is chosen by a group of astute judges, who all have previous when it comes to their own elegant time-management.

Our stuffed weasel is proudly stood over a decapitated shrew; use this shrew as your own personal metaphor. It may stand for a small triumph over an oppressive work place, an unfavourable arrangement such as a birthday party/wedding/Christening, or if you're really unlucky a September/October trip to the Swedish abyss... IKEA (it makes Dante's inferno look like a stroll down the beach), a reluctant spouse, or an unhelpful colleague. Les Dawson would surely use his mother-in-law. I leave the choice to you; the meaning of a weasel decapitating a shrew is a personal preference call.

Lamont and the weasel were intertwined at the hip. In 2012 he won our most coveted trophy in astonishing fashion – he had obviously visited the cross-roads again and swapped another of his photocopied souls, even the original was barely ankle deep. What follows is an extract from my 2012 diary:

> Lamont sent me a grim text that put one hand firmly on the weasel, my one consolation is the mental image of him texting with his gnarled giant comedy fingers. This message must have taken him an hour.
>
> *I had a job in Barrow, so on my way back I had a quick chuck on the Lune @ Caton. Nobody had caught ewt on the Monday and both EA beats had been fully booked. Five lads all told me that nothing had been taken all that day... tenth cast, bang, a fresh 12lb'r. I stuck it in the van and dropped it off at the smokers* in Glasson Dock on my way back to work. I arrived back at work just in time to finish...I'm on a roll.*

That particular hollow tipped digital bullet arrived while I was at work and it had maximum effect. In the past Lamont had sent photo messages with no content. He knew that all I saw on my phone was *picture message received* so I automatically thought he must have caught a Salmon. Intense feelings of dread when opening those messages inducing my gag reflex to engage and I choke on my own bile, brought on by my sheer joy for my friends news. I was always relieved when it was a clever hoax – however this claim was real and verified by a stunning picture of a sea liced fresh fish.

I was running out of runway and Lamont had kicked me squarely in the stones, leaving me trailing in the Weasel stakes. I had been ready with my work place joker of autumn pleurisy, which I had fully researched, ingesting the symptoms for a full blown psychosomatic visit to the GP's for an official diagnosis. The good Doctor had explained that it could flare up any time – how right he was, although he failed to mention that in my case it was linked to rainfall. But with only five weeks of the season left I only managed to catch two more Salmon – annoyingly both on free weekends.

One thing was for sure, I wanted that Weasel in 2013 as it was one of the few things that I remain overqualified for. My qualities, attributes and personality traits run well short of the rigid requirements of the elite of this world, but when it comes to the qualities, attributes and personality traits for an underhanded attempt at the Salmon Weasel, I am more than ideally suited to the contests precious specifics.

It's far more than just a trophy, it is a blazing symbol that your work/life balance is still narrowly in your favour. It's of vital importance.

As for today I was being brutally shanked in the showers by work with a shiv fashioned by Lamont and with no way out until 5pm. Mentally I still had the upper hand on my employers – they thought I was fully employed, a diligent member of a committed workforce but in effect I had retired aged thirty one, fourteen years ago after my first week at this work wonderland. Every single day since is dedicated to virtual and physical escape. I was being held, bound by socio-economics, a hostage against my own true will. I would nod and agree with HR and do the exact opposite, what could they do? Outlaw illness?

What is my job, where do I work? – I'm not sure I should release this information at this point. I have a lovely family whom I provide for – just. Let's face it this book isn't exactly going to be a smash hit. Two publishers rejected it very politely saying that it was well written but not commercial enough or disappointingly, that I wasn't a celebrity. Not for the first time I was referred to as "too niche."

So I've completely ignored their cowardly advice, saved up and self-published a short run of 500 copies to act as a kind of CV, if you are reading it I hope you're having fun. Although I may mock my job at the cracker factory – my three lovely's still need me to have it.

*Lamont got banned from the smoker

Chapter 5

Clint Best vs The Cosmos

One of my most pleasurable experiences had come while staring down the neck end of competitive sports fishing. It played out like this:

Aged 22 I had entered my local club's fly fishing competition – The NALGO shield. National Association of Local Government Officers – in case you were wondering. Placed three miles from my home as the crow flew there was a small three acre lake named Jeffery Pond in the middle of Woodfold Country Estate. The lake was fun to fish, well stocked with rainbows, fictional massive browns and although not far from the reaches of the town, it was absolutely rural.

Sixteen rods entered and two heats of eight went at it over four hours. Best weight won, top two went through to a semi final draw to fish the same rules head to head after drawing pegs. The winners of the semis faced each other on a Saturday morning July final.

In those days I liked to think of myself as the fly fishing outsider, a northern Huck Finn. I had a black brand-less carbon ten foot blank that I had whipped Fuji eyes on, it owned the subtle grace and action of a concrete lintel – one intrepid Rimfly reel and a wet cell two line with a knot in the end to attach 5lb Maxima line.

One of my favourite things was my hand turned weighted wooden priest that could have dropped a charging bull with one shot. This lot was kept in my Mum's woven shoulder beach bag along with about twenty lures and nymphs, a motley crew of black dog nobblers, white dog nobblers, orange fritzs, Montanas and weighted caddis kept snug in my Loch Leven fly tin. I had a four foot aluminium landing net pole and bright blue micro mesh round twenty two inch coarse landing net head, which I used for landing everything. I was so proud to own fuck all, not to have any choices to make other than to fish hard until it clicked.

I breezed through my round by fishing out an evening rise using a slow retrieve as soon as my line hit the water, letting my black dog nobbler sink and hypnotise the gormless rainbows. The grey tide that represented the rest of the competitors fumbled with dainty dry flys in an effort to match the hatch.

Tail of the tape

Blackburns: outlaw gunslinger, beach bag/George Best/Huck Finn – 8 rainbows for 15lb

Entire cast of the Last of the Summer Wine – 1 rainbow for 2lb

The result of the other round, one week later really

made my senses detonate – there was only one other young buck in this club – Mick Crook – six feet tall, jet black hair, brown eyes, lethal kidney punch, legendary head butt, athletic centre half, film star looks - all the girls loved him. Six days older than me, gifted natural caster and brutally competitive, he had also spent the last twelve years fishing for everything that swam within a ten mile radius of Blackburn with one of his best friends; me.

We drew each other to fish in the semis to take place one week later on a Friday evening. Everyone in our local pubs at the time – The Woodlands and The Clog and Billycock - knew what it meant. Mick was the current champ and was as ruthless as a viral infection – after a hapless stocking, all the trout had died within a few hours and needed fishing out, Mick turned up with face mask, snorkel, flippers and in an afternoon filled his mums chest freezer.

I was on his freckle though and he knew it. He said that my line, which I bought for five pounds after fishing it out of a bargain bin at a game fair, was lucky as it possessed an unclassified sink rate. The build-up banter was merciless and friends quickly began to speculate who would win. My preparation was to watch 'The Good, the Bad and the Ugly' every night until the semi. I felt this film would teach me a great deal – mainly give everyone an unfair advantage then come out confident and shooting.

On the night we travelled down together – tossing a coin for who had to open the two gates and run the gauntlet of the mad farmer's mad dog, Ming. I had the honour of pegging it, shouting fuck off Ming for a heart thumping one hundred and twenty metres. Mick watched, amused, from the safety of his blue Escort mark two.

Mick went big when he drew a jetty peg, ruled by the mythical splashes of one of the supposed resident browns. Nobody could ignore those splashes for long. Crooky knew... land Nessy and he would have been water tight. His casting was so elegant that his own narcissism was his undoing. He would watch his line cast down to the backing and land so straight and perfectly that he would shout across, "did you see that, brings a tear to the eye." This vanity made him fish the dry fly more than he should. By contrast I looked like a navvy digging a hole with a mallet, you could hear me ripping curtains as the line was dragged double handed off the water and launched back until I got the desired distance. It was agricultural to say the least – Ming probably would have been more graceful.

After four hours we weighed in. Mick knew he had been blown apart by a peasant ditch digger with a combination of Black Nobblers and caddis cunningly dragged across the bottom. Postcards of this flogging could have been made and stamps should have been issued. The super natural ghost brown hadn't massacred his surface Muddler or fallen for a buzzer attack, he had more chance of contacting the dead.

Clint Eastwood: Four rainbows for 7lb

Eli Wallach: Nil

We went to The Woodlands to share the news and a few beers about our contest. We discussed our upcoming Sunday League football match for the Clog and Billycock (I was centre forward – I once won an award in the shape of a Clog nailed to a plank – brass inscription read – *Miss of the season*, for a breathless two foot toe poke that went wide of an open net), and where we should go fly fishing on the Sunday after playing in the footy match. That's how free we were. Can you remember how that felt – take five minutes and ponder – make a brew and take yourself back to being twenty two – wasn't it a peach?

The final would prove to be a very different psychedelic kettle of fish.... Libérer le mental.

My four mile walk to the lake on that Saturday July morning remains a fragmented memory – I had spent from 2.30am restless in my bedroom in my parents' house accompanied only by a head full of acid, Shaun Ryder and sixty zillion flashing thoughts, unbridled chains of images, rhythms, beats, words, colours and sounds. Horizontal on my bed reminding myself to breathe as though I had escaped after being submerged under water ...huurrgghh, in, out, in, out – that's the ticket, breathing – why didn't I think of that earlier.

Friday evenings usually started like this –ten of us in the Woodlands pub at 7pm, Blakey's bar in Blackburn town 8pm, call in the Swan to score some acid, drop half a trip and smoke some herb. Proceed to laugh our bollocks off all the way round town feeling disengaged from your own self but also so aware of every conversation, linear - and able to join the strands no matter how tenuous and more importantly understand the game, to revel in it. To feel linked by those close friends who inhabited the same universe in a packed town centre. Two AM, twenty bensons, ten pints later and feeling like the starring role in your own movie, it was home time – I had a big day tomorrow, I could win a prize... Despatched in a taxi looking out the window marvelling at the rolling images, the night sky and noticing the contrast of EVERYTHING, mesmerised by the contours of a curb as you flowed along at thirty mph.

Home – tip toes to my room trying not to laugh – my Mum's an anaesthetic nurse – so one proceeded with extreme caution. Bedroom = safety and sanctuary. Now the smart money is on the casual acid taker being just sensible enough to have a stock of Temazepam or Valium to turn off this terrible drug. Not me, all I had was a massive six foot by three foot poster of Shaun William Ryder's face on the cover of Bummed, the Mondays finest LP, looking back at me while I led on my bed in my poster lined shrine to music trying to stay positive, think happy thoughts, obviously so very awake. All I could hear was Shaun singing Wrote For Luck (they sent me you) round and round for three and a half hours. Magic moments of self induced dementia.

In those days I was bullet proof, not like now – one string left to snap, five pints can leave me shaking like a shitting dog the morning after. By 6am the acid was clearing and I was entering the quiet calm stage – I still felt disconnected from my normal self but I could function to a point. I jumped out of bed, threw on my red Kicker pumps and consumed, what I considered the antidote to a complete night of carnage – a banana and drank a pint of water, collected my beach bag, net and rod and set off up the yellow brick road.

My eyesight was being streamed directly through a fish eye lens, the colours where switched on, nature had plugged itself in just for me and seemingly placed fairy lights in every leaf. I walked along the quiet main road, as though I was pacing through the pages of a distorted fairy tale pop-up book and turned into the opulent and majestic tree lined Meins Road. The sun was just warming up and it was clear that it was going to be a scorcher. No wind, no cloud, just sunshine. I felt completely confident and at ease. The entire world was beautiful and I was just a mere insignificant spec. I knew my place... Glad to be alive, pleased to be aware of other perceptions and boggling at the mind's power and those fine academics who invented LSD.

Dog walkers, joggers, milk men, paper boys, and cars

all gave me a wave, nod and a wink as I ambled with my rod on my shoulder returning their greetings – wow Blackburn was a friendly place. Then I remembered Ming. My own personal Cerberus lived at the end of Meins Road and probably hated Woodstock and peace. I was out of his reach today – nothing could penetrate my glow, nature had no need to be nervous of me. Once at the end of the road, I reached a cattle grid that signified the start of Ming's dynasty. The road became a ruptured farm track that led to the farm and the first of Ming's gates and one hundred and twenty yards of no-man's-land. This track was our only access. Ming lived for us fisherman to pass through – he was an utterly ferox Viet Cong border collie with a cunning urban outlook, I doubt he had ever been indoors – matted rasta coat, not an ounce of fat and always bad tempered - we represented his Babylon. The farm yard was a quiet dry dust bowl as I arrived at the gate – mother earth's vibrations told me I was safe. Open the gate and pick up speed and trot-on – head swivelling waiting to hear him scrambling for another young dead man. No sign and only twenty metres from the freedom of the second gate – karma shattered as the spicy bastard rounds the corner of the milking shed. Holy shit he looks amplified – I explode into a full blown sprint and clear the fence with a quantum leap, just two metres to spare of Ming's flaring jaws. After a few disappointed huffs and puffs, he turns and resumes his position in an open drain next to the milking barn, troll-like – waiting for his next course of entertainment. I give him a quick cocky flick of the V's and call him a twat.

Descending down the track I'm flanked by neon turbo green fields, which spread out down the Ribble Valley towards Houghton and Preston. Directly on my right shoulder is a dark lurching twisted broadleaf wood that evoked the fear as I walked by it. I hear a car behind me and see that it's my opponent and two of his fellow NALGO committee members all attired with burgundy faces and broad grins as they see me. With my heightened senses I could hear what they were wearing before they disembarked from their motor, the muffled rustle of a wool cotton blend jumper, a flurry of corduroy and the clank of several pairs of Hush Puppies. As they get out of the car, one of the committee men was examining his jumbo cords trouser leg six inches above his ankle – he is cursing Ming and muttering that *it's a bloody menace*. His interests soon return to me though as they ask me what I've come as…

For the first time that morning I take a close look at myself – red kicker pumps, black cotton knee length cut off chinos and a black cotton Paul Smith shirt that had the largest and brightest floral repeat pattern of red, blue and yellow roses all over it. This was my Friday night going out shirt which I considered a sure fire bated honey trap, a conversation starter, an *in*. Thanks to my tattered state of mind I hadn't even noticed that it was still on my back. I flashed back to all those smirking bastard joggers, paperboys, milkmen, dog walkers and drivers all giving me the nod and the thumbs up... Wow, wasn't Blackburn full of funny bastards?

Thanks to the glory of the acid I had managed to bypass any kind of fashion filter. I stood before these NALGO committee men like a black haired, ten bob eyed tourist, complete with beach bag and homemade rod. Hugh Falkus I was not, more like an overblown cartoon character than a traditional vision of a fly fisherman.

I remember while waiting for the draw and during awkward conversation, very distinctly the heavy feeling of thirst and of the bright hot sunshine. The acid wave had got me this far but it was about to break and leave me high and dry. The first feelings of mild discomfort were circling around my head like giant condors. I needed to be in my own space, by myself, just the two of us, one doing the fishing and the other providing a running commentary of all proceedings, future, past and present.

The draw for pegs was finally made – my competitor drew the best peg on the lake, while I drew an overgrown peg at the opposite end. Lilies twenty five feet in front of me that narrowed thirty feet to my left until they met the bank, creating a forty five degree wedge shaped channel. Any way you wanted to slice it – it was a dog day to fish for trout, hot, bright and still. I had no reason to be confident, however this information hadn't punctured into my own psyche – my mind had swirled back into optimism mode and was now doing handstands wondering how much a tin of Brasso was for polishing the trophy. I opened my fly box, at eight inches away the colours leapt out. I laughed as I tied on an orange fritz and cast out down the Lily lined margins. The morning was full of internal and external chuckling. Before eleven o'clock I had caught three two pound rainbows. My blanking opponent conceded with thirty minutes still remaining.

We shook hands and concluded our business; I was the NALGO champ and would receive my trophy at the AGM. I declined a lift in favour of walking up a path through the woods towards Pleasington and the Clog and Billycock that avoided Ming's grasp. By now I was urgently in need of a drink and someone I could talk to who was on my level. A few of my mates would be in the Clog for our regular blissful Saturday afternoon of killer pool, darts, three card brag and banter.

I opened the door and instantly was greeted by friends, lent on the bar reloading and by Jimmy Hendrix singing Voodoo Chile – *I stand up next to a mountain...* Beautiful soul filling noise, the shirt and rod cocktail had thrown them… "Did you fish or what?"… I pause, lean my rod on the bar and for one of the only times in my life I happily reply ... *I won.* For the next eight hours I retold the encounter to a backdrop of much laughter, beer and amazing music. Youth wasted on the young? Well George, it certainly didn't feel like it... which I guess is its essence.

Boo Gilbraith - NALGO fly fishing Champ 1990, King Kipper* 1998/99, self appointed life president of The Guild Of Reason – club motto Be Reasonable

George Bernard Shaw – Nobel prize for literature 1925

Since this foray into the world of club contests we decided to create our own closed competitions between ourselves, a group of about eight to twelve fly fishing friends to ensure that one of us wins something while receiving just the right amount of needle.

*The King Kipper shield is a biannual fly fishing match on day ticket waters – heaviest bag wins. Mick Crook has been crowned KK three times. Win it five times and he gets to keep the trophy. It's a horrible thought.

Chapter 6

Only love can do that

Having clock watched in the cracker factory and survived a feverishly hellish day free from digital bullets and a gloating Lamont, I headed for my car knowing it was now my turn to roll the dice. I could be on the river in thirty minutes flat with still three hours of daylight remaining. There was ever the remote possibility of a small run of fish filtering through our beat, (that said; in my head there never isn't a remote possibility). I would of course first have to posture and negotiate my early release from parental duties.

This particular early evening collar could be difficult to slip; a one year old baby girl and four year old son would be waiting for their personal climbing frame and punch bag to get home from work, coiled like multiple Katos ready for some easy sport. It's as cruel as bear baiting or hoofing a donkey out of a bell tower – I would slump in from work and lumber defenceless into what was once a front room generously designed for relaxation. Now this same room is transformed into vicious pit where I will be worn down by a nasty combination of noise, violence and ABH, confused, softened for the kill.

Within three minutes of wistful hangdog gazing out the window my wife had popped the question, "why don't you go fishing – you look like a trapped wasp bumping against the window." Only love can do that, only love could be that understanding. Breathing in the freedom I quickly fired all my gear in the boot and cranked up the volume in the car for my gloriously short 5 minute car journey to the river. I selected the appropriately titled Yes! from American band Colourmusic and filled my head with their sonic wavebands. I arrived on the club car park to find only one car parked up. I knew it would be there, it was owned by a heron with a rod licence named Karl. I always like bumping into Karl because he is fish bonkers, sick with it, he grafts harder than photosynthesis. I quickly opened the boot looking up the beat, in the blossoming spring sunshine, listening to the crackle of the river while assembling my tackle. I had a gander at the level and colour of the river while stringing up my rod – it looked perfect. The right hand bank was populated by ancient arcing woodland clasping to a steep gradient which pitched the treetops towards the river, following its contours that offer the river both shade and cover. I jumped over the gate and set off up to the top of the beat so I could fish back to the car – the light was starting to leave so I reckoned on about two hours left.

I had a quick natter with Karl who was stationed half way through a pool in the middle of the beat and we quietly and quickly swapped contradicting theories while both agreeing that it *felt* fishy. I got up to the top pool and casted in – the fly carried round beautifully. I was fishing a floater with a slow sink tip, 15lb three foot leader with a size 8 shrimp pattern on a double. After a few casts I naturally considered that everything I was doing was wrong and that I should be deeper. During this internal dialogue my mind wanders as I start to fish on auto pilot... I start to consider why I hadn't learnt how to body-pop or break dance when younger. I hadn't even mastered robotics – I was always into hip hop but I hadn't had the courage to engage with the entire culture. Maybe it was due to me never owning a complete tracksuit that matched. Had

this been a miscalculation – are these attributes I lacked? Should I now aged 45 dig out my EPMD Strictly Business LP, find my Kangol wool grouser, join a street dance class and bust some moves? I'm now daydreaming, imagining myself doing the caterpillar to Serengeti's track Rib Tips across a laminate floor at the next cracker factory Christmas party, would I wear hi –tops or Gazelles…? Shazam! The line goes tight and I feel the force of the take. Unimaginable surprise as I awake into this storming of my senses – make no mistake about it, this is a springer and it's holding in the thickest current about to drop down a groin being pushed by its own instinct and the pure force of water. Let it run, let the fucker run – I can hear you – I know that's the dance. Follow it down the groin and play it out in slacker water. Only a clueless clown would attempt to heave the fish towards him against about a million metric tons of water – that's exactly what this blockhead did. The laws of physics wouldn't be denied - the hook pulled – our contest had lasted about 50 seconds. Nine months since a pull on a fly (kelts don't count). I felt like I'd been victim of a mugging; one minute I was mentally doing the caterpillar, the next receiving a sudden unexpected pitiless shoeing. The automatic response to this is to cast again and desperately try to replicate the incident and have a more positive outcome. But it didn't happen. I was alone, the fool on the hill – wondering why?…why everything?… I was stood on a rocky outcrop looking squarely down the river. My head is bowed and I am momentarily a lost little boy. There is no rewind button to put things right or as I felt they should be. The sudden shock and devastating impact slowly filters through and swells inside like a balloon on a water tap.

After spending the remainder of my session gormlessly swishing about in a punch drunk feckless daze, I trudge back to the car in near darkness. The crucial moment had gone, vanished, evaporated – and I had blown it big time. My evening was capped off when my landing net frame softly brushed the farmer's electric fence that seductively skirts our beat – this sudden jolt caused me to perform an involuntary goose step and shout FUCK simultaneously. It served me right – I should have been made to lick that fence until sunrise.

I wandered through my front door some ten minutes later bewildered and shuffling like I had just received electro shock therapy. My wife kindly asked me what had happened and enquired if I had been in a road traffic collision. So rare is it that I arrive home and say I have had any form of contact with a salmon she naturally presumed by my stunned expression, that I must have been involved in an accident. I simply explained that she had married a dick... I wasn't met with an argument. Later that night I at least put on a good show by concentrating on the positives – they (salmon) were obviously about, so that was a decent starting point. It's just good to get out etc. I had seen some wonderful wildlife, what a joy it was to be in such a beauti...bullshit...bastard twat...

Next day at work my intuitive colleagues at the cracker factory wisely gave me a wide – everybody notices the vacant guy shuffling around shaking his head and muttering seemingly out of context expletives...knob, you knob, what a knob, thick cunt, bollocks and forfuckssake, afuckingspinger...dick.

The level of the river quickly dropped off and I was left to dwell on my unfinished symphony for another five whole days. During my thirty minute commute to work every day I rely on my iPod to shuffle me up some sunshine – but now it proved the time honoured cliché by kicking my teeth in with a chorus of break-up music.

- Long Time Gone – By Crosby, Stills and Nash
- Lost Cause – by Beck
- The Sadness In Your Life Will Slowly Fade – by Bill Wells and Aidan Moffat
- I Am Goodbye – By Bonnie Prince Billy
- Let's Stay Together – By Al Green

And so on... the bastard.

Lamont had taken the news of my incompetence in his stride and had offered me these kind words, "you're very possibly the biggest cockend I've ever met," followed up with the roundhouse, "it must be a burdensome load."

My optimism was only pulled back from the light by the arrival of rain on Sunday afternoon and by Tuesday evening I was back on the river in the very same fish losing spot having fled the cracker factory an hour early after claiming my children were ill...

Safe in the knowledge that I was ethically astute in using my children as a Trojan horse to aid my escape – I joined the omnipresent Karl on the beat to discover that nobody had seen anything and that it was "fucking quiet..." It was a mild clear spring evening, nicely overcast and without a hint of wind as I cast into the pool using exactly the same set up as the week before.

An hour passed without any sign of life, so I gave the pool a rest for twenty minutes before I resumed my efforts. Second cast and the line went tight, with a cracking take and I lift into a fish. It's a carbon copy in the exact same spot, this time I let the fish run down the groin and into the quick water. I've got the rod tip up and I walk down the rocks and calmly follow. Now the fish is in the mid current and I have options as I have avoided the heavy force of the water by not fighting it. The salmon feels well hooked and I am able to reel in and get right over the top of it but just as I do this it turns and runs, fast, hard and heavy straight upstream at lightning pace into the heavy stuff. The river becomes my aid as the fish tires in the current and I am able to bring the fish back in front of me. We repeat this dance twice more before I can walk the fish to a desirable landing site. My heart is on my tongue as I hold the gye net at full stretch in my left hand while keeping the rod up as high as I can manoeuvring the fish over the net – hallefuckinglujah it's in...massive breath out.

The fish is so silver it's blue, (alas no sea lice, I imagine that they fell off during the struggle) and is about eleven pounds. I am absolutely elated as it's my first ever Ribble springer. Another angler, Paul, arrives and kindly takes a photo and gets in the pool above me. The fish goes back and I sit on the bank to enjoy the moment. I send my digital bullets to my comrades and proudly await their plaudits. Catching a Ribble springer was no walking day at Bathhurst – I had been trying for just the twenty one years. I walk back to the car hopeful to be able to tell about two hundred anglers on the way back but there is, as always, only Karl – who had astonishingly just put a fresh ten pounder back. The fish in their wisdom had arrived at once, which isn't that unfamiliar a tale – it's the norm really. We have all suffered from an utterly banal period on the river then suddenly all hell breaks loose.

As I walked off the beat a happy fulfilled man gently striding out with a smile on my face I gave myself a mental pat on the back for suppressing my true feelings. Inside I was galloping across the field like Marco Tardelli after firing a game winning torpedo past Harald Schumacher, arms outstretched and ten bob eyed, screaming and crying simultaneously. Back In the private sanctuary of my car it was a very different matter – Happy by The Aliens was selected on the iPod and I savoured every minute of my drive, contented and pleased that after my promiscuous antics with the Dee that it was my local love that had come up aces.

Lamont phoned while on my way home. I wasn't surprised that after offering his congratulations, which I am pleased to say, he managed to make sound like he was pushing a boulder up an acute hill while swiftly turning the subject to the length of waiting list for the beat I had just fished... It was all immensely satisfying.

My season was off and running and it was only May - life is beautiful. I could turn my frontal lobes back onto the serious stuff – like robotics and electric handshakes.

Chapter 7

The Deconstruction of Evolution

A hymn for everyman

As May drifted into June it became evident that rain was to become a rarity and that perhaps we should just enjoy the sunshine, stand down, unload the boot for the time being and break out the picnic blanket. Maybe I could use this down time as a period of recovery – half time - iron out all my aches and pains. Get myself match fit for the big three months. My list of ailments included a pulled left hamstring, a ropey left Achilles tendon and an awkward nagging knot under my right shoulder blade which felt like it needed digging out. This sucker was my priority as it had been ambivalent to my own course of treatment - the rotator cuff cure all, the Mick Channon windmill.

It was while I was completing my homespun physiotherapy that a colleague advised that a massage would sort it out, and that she knew a girl doing a degree course at a nearby college who needed a model so she could be assessed on her Swedish massage. I couldn't let Sweden down. My colleague went on to inform me that the treatment would be completely free of charge. I couldn't let my bank account down.

So I found myself on planet beauty therapy surrounded by beauticians and people wearing scrubs. As I examined this new environment it became notable that nobody owned their own; skin tone, fingernails, eyelashes or eyebrows. As I listened to whales singing, I inspected the posters on the wall with open mouthed wonder – *Genuine Racoon hair extensions on sale here*. Boy was I out of touch. I was ushered into a cubicle and asked a list of questions by a very friendly lady who seemingly needed assurance that I wouldn't croak under her care. Once Michelle was satisfied that I was fit enough to be treated then she pulled the drape around the massage table, asked me to strip to my boxers and exited the curtain. No problem – I stood there, gut out with no hiding place and gave her a meek shout that I was ready for her to return.

She was a cheerful happy woman in her early thirties, very smiley and polite in a hyper air-hostess sort of way. I am stood next to the table-bed thing wondering about shaved racoons.

The following exchange is conducted with the patient using an unnervingly suspicious tone. While the other protagonists concentrate on a disbelieving quizzical note.

Michelle: "Right then, the first thing I am going to do is check your posture. Can you stand up straight please?"

Me: "I am."

"Ohhh, really, straighten your back and puff your chest out."

I stretch back and straighten up.

"Ohhhh – does that feel straight to you, can you step back to the wall and put your heels to the wall and touch the wall with your shoulder blades?"

I obey her instructions.

Michelle goes from shoulder to shoulder with a look of mild concern and then stands in front of me with her hands on both shoulders at once.

Me: "What's wrong?"

"I'm going to have to ask Donna to come in and look at this."

Me: "Why what's up?"

Michelle went off to get Donna and it's just me against the wall and the whales.

Michelle returns with an older, more mature looking woman who wouldn't look out of place behind a make-up counter or hiding in a bowl of oranges.

Michelle gives Donna a quick recap and Donna asks me to take a step forward.

Donna: "Oh yes Michelle, I see what you mean... is that how you stand normally?"

Me: "Er, yes I think so, why?"

Donna: "Errmmm well you seem to have a stoop – have you ever been in an accident?"

Me: "No, no accidents."

Donna: "I think we need to get Marie to have a look." Donna disappears.

Michelle now says that it's nothing to worry about, while I think to myself, Marie? Who the fuck's Marie?

Donna returns accompanied by a lady in her late fifties with glasses suspended on the end of her nose, mature hog roasted complexion, alarming carrot tan, six inch lama hair eyelashes, hand drawn surprised eyebrows, inch long zebra pattern fingernails and a upright microwaved racoon hair do that Don King would have been proud of. She was obviously their queen.

Queen Marie now gets the capsule recap and asks me using her thirty a day East Lancashire guttural croak to walk ten feet in a straight line, turn and come back. The three of them take a look at me as though they have found the missing link. All I can think of is the Patterson Gimlin film footage of Bigfoot walking through the forest.

Marie: "Please take a step back and put your shoulders against the wall."

Marie, tight lipped and head slightly shaking puts her hands on my shoulders and gives me a quizzical look.

Marie: "Thanks Donna, yes Michelle you may continue with the treatment and advise the client that he should do some exercises to improve his posture. He appears to stoop forward in a hunched fashion and you're right, he does seem to have one shoulder bigger than the other."

I now feel like Marty Feldman playing Igor in the film Young Frankenstein.

Donna and Marie leave while Michelle gets me to lay face down on the massage table.

Michelle gets to work and starts giving it plenty. She soon finds a knot the size of a pike bung and explains that my shoulder is as swollen as a cartoon ham and that I will have to come back four or five times before it's cured. During the next forty minutes we have a chin wag about how my shoulder could be in such a state.

I really was a total blank. I mentally tallied all my many activities but I couldn't offer an answer. Maybe it's due to you bending down and picking the kids up all the time, says Michelle... No other solution to my giant shoulder sprung to mind.

It wasn't until I got in the car that I arrive at a rare eureka moment.

Flying condom, twenty eight grams, sixty to a hundred visits a year, for on average four hours per visit, seventy casts an hour for over twenty seasons, casting a combined accumulative weight just short of the Humber Bridge.

60 visits x 280 casts = 16,800 casts per year

16,800 casts x 21 years x Humber Bridge = enraged shoulder like a beach ball.

Maybe I should cut down on my spinning and concentrate on the fly rod. During the next four sessions

on that table I couldn't even contemplate explaining the obvious cause of my condition. That would mean describing the whole process of salmon fishing to Michelle, and then admitting that I had forgotten to mention that I was a fisherman - face down with my head looking out a port hole, examining the base of a massage table… That ship had sailed, so as usual I took the easy option and blamed parenthood.

&

So June became my usual welcomed interlude, a month without temptation or haste. I took the chance to take some evening walks and check out some beats for pools that could be worth a dip with the shrimp or that could be worth a late night appointment with some sea trout.

As soon as the cracker factory klaxon sounded I could pole vault the fence, flee to the river and gleefully loaf about with the shrimp rod, happily watching the red top of my float roam down a pool like a drunk wandering home. This particular pool was on my direct flight path from work and it was criminal to pass it without having a look. I didn't do this every night but only when the water had lifted and then dropped off quickly allowing fish to move up and settle. It remains one of only two pools that constantly get referenced by other Ribble anglers as a safe bet to see some fish in low water.

It's normally a speedy affair – run the float through

two twenty metres sections for an hour and bolt home. One minute I'm knelt trotting my float admiring the summer calm enjoying the silence and wondering what's for tea, then a leaping fish only a matter of feet away, that must be closer to twenty than fifteen, clears my float and then proceeds to get covered for a good half an hour without so much as a bob. It's those types of incident that can send you home hatching plans...

Later that night I was caught reading Fred Buller's essays on shrimping to my boy as a bed time story. I was trying to impart the seductive nature and anticipation of watching a float drift downstream waiting for a bite...he seemed to like it...his mother took a different view.

After the shoulder lull and this brief bit of rain she was full of enthusiasm for me to go and enjoy myself on the river. Our recent day trips out had included picnics by the Ribble and ice creams at Ribchester. How we joked about how I always got us by the river somehow... slowly this blooming enthusiasm had understandably dissolved...to the point that I had to lie about my true thoughts. While clearly in a day-dream come semi trance wondering about the changing geography of the river/ bait/presentation/tactics/weather-patterns/forecasts/ clubs/tackle/tide times/water temperature/salmon/sea-trout... my wife suddenly asks me what I'm thinking about. Jolted from my day dream I have to quickly scramble for my mental good behaviour cue cards. I can tell by her expression that she doesn't want to hear that

I'm thinking about fishing...I convincingly tell her that I am concerned about which primary school our one year old daughter should eventually go to. This is met with suspicious approval and the inevitable ugly by-product leaps like a mugger at a cash point: a full-on conversation about education...I make a mental note to steer clear of reactionary hot topics...of course I can't tell her this, and carry on rewinding my mind tape of the leaping salmon while nodding with my concerned face.

The last thing I saw that night before visiting the land of nod was that same leaping salmon – both taunting and haunting wrapped up in one perfectly framed airborne thrust. I found myself recumbent in a Hermes reclining chair with my feet cradled in the matching foot stool. I was in a dimly lit oak lined office; I could just make out a large oil painting of a proud cormorant, hanging to my left, to my right the walls were crowded with dusty books dancing for attention. Across from me was an ugly large dark wood desk and behind it sat my wife dressed as Albert Einstein, she rocked forward and mouthed the word "parasite."

Alberta was holding up a tortoise shell hand mirror, that she flipped around so I could see my own reflection. My mouth had become an oral cone and I had an insatiable primeval thirst for blood and fresh epidermal tissue. My antennae groped towards Einstein as I tried to take stock. My obsessive behaviour had triggered a metamorphosis – I was a fully functioning six foot sea louse and I was being counselled by Alberta Einstein – what could a sea louse do? Tell her I would change my ways and look for an alternative to parasitic behaviour – go into politics or that I was just naughty by nature?

Alberta, resplendent in her Einstein wig then said in a terrible Austrian accent, "do you know vot the definition of insanity is Mr Louse?...Let me tell you, it's doing the same thing over and over and expecting different results."

I woke shivering in a puddle of sweat, in a state of high anxiety and extreme relief. I quickly woke my wife and

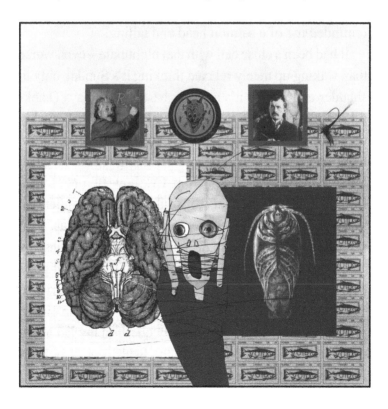

explained my terrible nightmare. She gently told me with her brassneck that if I had have been a parasitic sea louse, I may have probably been less needy. Still in a heightened state I needed definitive answers, so I pleaded - what had Alberta meant? Should I change tactics, go up-stream and sit tight or travel down to the lower river and hope for a tide fresh fish? Bemused and alarmed and staring straight at her I received "picture no sound" (Lamonts perfect phrase for the silent treatment), and with a shake of her head and a subtle roll of her shoulder she turned on her side and sunk back under the duvet. This obviously reminded me of a salmon head and tailing.

It had been a close call with that nightmare – even worse than waking up nicely relaxed thinking it's Sunday only to shudder and realise it's actually bastard Monday. Thankfully it was 6am on a Saturday and I had a plan. I quickly booted my five year old son out of bed and dressed him like Elmer Fud telling him we were going to catch big bad Barry – his favourite fish (from TV show Ben & Hollies Little Kingdom) and that we would have to be quiet and avoid contact with the farmer as he would chase us. That was all the boy needed to hear, the potential of a chase by a half crazed farmer on a quad bike and a mythical giant boat eating fish as a prize was like a self-voted pay rise to a politician (all in favour of awarding ourselves an eleven percent pay rise say aye). The only question my lad asked was could we chase Mum with the fish's head. My heart filled with pride as I replied yes son, of course we can.

We jumped in the car and Fran chose Jonnie Common's fantastic LP – Master of None as our Saturday morning soundtrack of DIY lo-fi electronica. We were loaded with my salmon net, twelve foot Barbel rod, spinning reel and armed with a pocket full of day glow disco prawns, two floats, small box of drilled bullets, shrimp pins, trebles and line. Our session could last no longer than 7am - 9.30am as he had a swimming lesson, so we would just cover the top of the beat as this was where I had seen the fish the previous night and it was fairly easy to access. I laid it on thick as we crossed the three hundred yards from the car to the river, making us go behind hedges and staying out of sight from the farm house. I had permission to fish but my lad didn't know that – it's a much better game to keep him in the dark and smuggle our way to the river. I hadn't really wanted to cultivate the already shadowy skulking image of the track suited or camouflage clad bait angler. This was more a lesson in stealth. We belly crawled the last twenty yards until we dropped down the steep bank to the river side. All the way I had to field eclectic questions about the various capabilities of the farmers JCB's and tractors including top speeds and noise levels of the engines. Then the odd curve ball direct from a five year olds mind – "do you think he has a lion, Dad?"

I set up quickly and cast slightly upstream and trotted the float down about a rods length out. We were crouched low and quiet, me fishing and my lad on lion watch.

Second cast, a salmon rises and shows its silver flank as it flashes at the bait, without taking, turns and vanishes. The boy is oblivious as I tug his arm and gesture at the float while asking if he saw the fish – "no Dad, was it Barry?" Pulling the bail arm over and holding his hands on the rod we flick the float out again about ten feet in front of us – up from the deep comes a salmon all of fifteen pounds and clears our float by at least a foot – landing back in the river with a hefty sploosh. The boy's eyes widen as he shouts "it's big bad Barry Dad, why didn't you catch him?" For the next hour all we do is cast curses as we cover that spot and nothing else stirs. I knew we didn't have much chance when the first fish came and turned away, they are usually either in the mood or not. My son remained admiringly philosophical as we trotted back to the car, "Uncle Lamont would have caught Barry Dad, it jumped right over your rod...Has he seen the farmer's lion Dad?...Maybe Barry had already had his breakfast." This was no time or place to start explaining the shrinking digestive system of the returning Atlantic salmon – some things are just best left unsaid.

Chapter 8

Sure fire ways to sweeten the mind

Sunstack Jones

On the Ribble I have a multitude of riches with plenty of syndicated water to go at – all for about the average price of a Championship League football season ticket. The choice is mine, right from Preston up to Clitheroe and beyond, all frequented by an enigmatic cast list of poets and pugilists, regular seasonal migrants of varying degrees of psychological distress and salmon induced dementia. Every one of them brimming with pointed fingers, potted logic and custom made theories, all aired while glued to the bank like a colony of fur seals definitely not fishing, tailor made for any situation that can generally substitute for any real effort while on the river.

> *I only cast when I see one* (a genuine quote from the rarely seen man in the wood). Baring in mind that I fish up to a hundred times a year and if I see twenty fish I consider myself to be living in Shangri la. Lamont suggested that he needed sectioning under the Mental Health Act or was already off his meds.

These people are welded to the nuances of every river and the sport. You can seemingly be in the middle of nowhere, quietly imagining yourself as a salmon resting behind a rock or hugging the bottom slowly making headway upstream and suddenly comes the sound of your name from a northern accented bush or tree line, followed by a smiling face from someone you bump into once or twice a year, grinning at the knowledge that you are both confidently booting sand into life's smug face, just by being out making your own decisions and happy to appreciate the absurd nature of your chosen hobby. Some club waters even dove-tail into each other giving me the choice of two beats at once, three miles of fishing and some head scratching decisions. Naturally the best pools are the furthest away from the car park and a wandering grass is greener/they've all come past us mentality can sweep through me like a virus at a festival. Let me walk you through the earhole and give you a guest list exclusive incite into a typical day inside a head full of choices.

Ok, so I'm sat on my bed semi-conscious at 6.30am wondering if it's worth committing to flicking the switch to the ON position. The first mission is to steel myself past the kids rooms, they sleep on hair-triggers and seem to be equipped with motion sensors, get downstairs in full stealth mode and evade capture. I have to get from my bedroom, downstairs and through the lounge to the laptop like a tomb raider, so that I can take a look at the height of the river at various Environmental Agency (EA) sites to ascertain which beat will be the most conducive to fish. This, the size and time of the tide are the most important information on display. For a complete ON commitment, ideally I want a large early morning tide with the river falling and losing its colour. This process can be distracting as once on the internet I could hook up to various sites, webcams and end up checking how many they have recently caught on the moon.

Luckily living near to the catchment means you get to follow the pulse of the river and conditions are never that far from your mind, making you seemingly fluent in all manner of obscure environmental equations. Anticipation is the name of the game. Being able to cough and splutter through work sounding like a burnt out vacuum, while asking colleagues if they have any Paracetamol as you watch the rain come down knowing that if the weather forecast holds you can legitimise your absence from work in two days' time is part of the game.

With all the signs in place I can switch to ON and start to move more fluidly, without indecision or guilt hampering my judgement. Guilt is a yoke to be avoided at all costs – nothing spoils a day on the river like a slow sense of guilty foreboding snagging up each cast and tightening your shoulders. Console yourself with the knowledge that the world keeps turning – if it's a work day then I have to phone the cracker factory and let them know of my demise. Everybody has a sick voice – my tactic is to be so horribly graphic that the recipient on the other end of the phone is so totally repulsed by my illness that they conjure up pitiful images of me and thus evoking their to-

113

tal and complete apathy as they go about their drone like duties in the hive. Obviously when I phone I try to do this somewhere devoid of background noise. Lamont once ran it close when he shouted if I wanted brown sauce on a bacon and egg T-cake, while I was in mid strained diphtheria pant to my boss - I told my boss that a news reader was talking about a brown horse on my TV.

Once in transit it's crucial to be decisive, don't fanny around. Be sure to hit the ground running, making the best decision on the information obtained. Many, many times I have found myself at a T junction stopped like a stuttering frame on a DVD, head on the steering wheel, open mouthed and dribbling – burned and buried by information overload, holding up traffic; weighing up the odds, unable to decide on left or right, up or down stream. By now messages and phone calls are being exchanged at an alarming rate consisting of thirty miles of river reports and on the hoof analysis all in the same hour from six or seven different people that you barely even know, all searching for clues. Much like the fish we are chasing – we use our super powers to react to the circumstances around us, married to the seasons, conditions aligning as we all hope to solve the riddle. All these components slowly fitting together creates a flowing feeling of suspense and in turn this subtext becomes another exciting element to savour and cherish as your anticipation grows.

High lush green pheasant lined hedgerows cloak the back lanes towards the river cutting through rural residential properties and farm land. These hedgerows only allow a gripping form of tunnel vision as they successfully mask any view of the horizon. Juxtapose this situation with a car full of music and you create a real sense of movement and poetic existence. As the singer Kenny Anderson AKA King Creosote poetically puts it in his epic song about a trawler fisherman – John Taylor's Month Away – "I'd rather be me." The slow drive down these lanes is a steady thrill filled with purpose as you finally close in on the river. One last left turn and you are able to hear the fanfare as you see the glories of the Ribble Valley stretch out below as you drop down a steep farm road to the club car park. The sky suddenly unfolds above and reaches seemingly around the world. From this hilltop vantage point you can see the entire beat before you as you descend. A wave of calmness and deep meaning satisfaction submerges the senses as contentment fills your heart – your eyes relax while you outwardly sigh with happiness. Isn't time travel a great feeling – here you are now, momentarily free, on the river about to be part of it, crossing universes to become fully involved. Close your eyes remember and just BE at your favourite fishing spot...so simple, so pure and cleansing.

Lamont is nearly always already on the club car park due to some undiagnosed sleep phobia which makes him leave the house at 4am and sit in his car, examining his gear and meddling with his disintegrating wading boots. His ritual is to brief me on the seemingly perfect state of the river, the tide times including approximate time of arrival of the fresh fish. He knows I know this information but once aired it becomes his copyrighted hypothesis. We usually recognise the motors on this car park if any, so it serves as an indication of where on the beat could be free – to avoid disappointment we usually go up through the wood to the top of the beat to fish one of our favourite runs.

At the top of this wood is a pool that in the past has been very productive for us both, so it's always our first choice. It's the fishing with confidence thing that acts like a magnet on the memory. Every salmon angler mentally red flags the exact spot on any river where they experienced a take, tussle or capture of a fish. If only I could unlock and apply these mind skills on other more average daily activities.

Other super hero powers that salmon fishermen possess but look dodgy on a CV include:

• The amazing ability to smell when the river is "right" from any geographical site

• Interpreting bird song as a cue to go fishing

• To be able to tell when a day feels "fishy"

• Act as a human barometer and automatically memorise the air pressure of a successful day

• The ability to cloak these super powers behind a public veil of stupidity, as cunning as Clark Kent's glasses

The wood is an orthopaedic surgeon's wet dream, a river hugging half a mile of mixed woodland terrain delivered on an angle between fifty and seventy degrees that makes the walk feel like you're riding a dilapidated wall of death on a 50cc Honda plastic chicken. The wood is punctuated by fallen trees, hog weed, nettles, thistles, Himalayan balsam, knee deep bogs and cavernous hidden holes. It was this sadistic ramble that made me ditch my 4.5mil cannibal boil-a-man in a bag neoprene waders in favour of some light weight breathable numbers. Over time we have forged a fragile desire line over this anglers Grand National course. When the going is good to firm I have completed it in less than eight minutes with just a one rod handicap and Lamont chomping at the bit behind me, trying to brew up an argument about whose honour it is. When the going is soft and heavy it's a twenty minute commando slog – on the way up your right side bears the brunt of multiple slips and falls. On the way back down your natural balance is restored as the left side now gets the pub fight treatment aided by your own terra-unfirma felt sole wading boots. Falling over is so ingrained and integrated that Lamont and I have now even stopped laughing at each other as we take a tumble. New skills abound as we learned the importance of throwing our rods just before the point of impact so not to damage them when the natural reaction is to use them as a form of brace. Far better to break your nose or a couple of fingers than have to deal with a customer care repairs department and spend your life rooting round for packaging to send a snapped section back and step on the nearly as fast as creeping moss, twenty one day turnaround time, merry-go-round. By the time your rod gets back to you your season could be lying in a shallow grave – forgotten in the woods.

During a season this woodland trot can be completed twenty or thirty times – usually it's in some stolen time as part of an ongoing campaign of guerrilla hit and run tactics before or after work when you have an hour window of opportunity. Bolt up there and fish through the pool once and then hurriedly traverse the wood back to the car park, change and arrive at home/work – quietly glowing with satisfaction.

Note to self: – Never, ever, ever convince yourself
again that it's a good idea to do it at night to catch Sea
Trout. Jesus…the horror.

On arrival at the top pool and after some lively debate loosely revolving around ethics and morality, one of us sits while the other makes their way through the pool. The person on the lowest seasonal total of salmon gets the honour. At this point in proceedings I can stop and ponder, surface and breathe in the beauty surrounding me, marvel at the clarity of our open plan theatre, and soak in the sounds of the world un-mechanised. I may only be ten miles from home but the feeling of detachment from the choking socio-economic urban umbilical cord seems infinite. It's a precious time to reclaim some mental territory in my own headspace.

Our bench is nothing short of a modern miracle. It was made by our friend Kirk who felt that our efforts needed an adequate bankside monument. For years we have dashed passed Kirk like a circus act as he quietly fished for Barbel in the wood and he was always keen to swap news and views. We liked the fact that over time he came to understand that 99% of the time our efforts would be fruitless and yet somehow we still maintained our enthusiasm.

The bench came as a fantastic shock to us – Kirk had built it at the perfect angle to look down the beat at one of my happiest places. The river shadowed by the wood, under a huge sky. Kirk had even planted a few young trees around the bench so that it could grow old at a graceful pace. From the bench you could comfortably look down at your comrade fishing and still remain invisible, high up the bank and cloaked by trees. When Kirk excitedly surprised us with it we had a small ceremony – whiskey and words while we secured the plaque, for everything we had lost and found by the river. We needed an appropriate phrase – after a week of thought I came to the conclusion that the only phrase fitting for the brass plaque was *Ring in Sick*, it's a fitting pertinent reminder of the importance of a correct work-life balance, time management and the key to mental wellbeing. As presents, kindness and selfless gestures go, our simple humble wooden bench built by somebody who barely knows us remains one of my enduring favourites.

Now we are here at our favourite secluded spot, I watch Lamont for half an hour fish slowly down the pool. Taking his time he is both quiet and methodical as he fishes out every cast with silent optimism. We do not chat - only listen to the day talk to us using its natural lyrical tones and language. Lamont finally turns his head to look up at me and shouts, "I told you we should have gone down the bottom, there's fuck all here." Rose tinted glasses smashed by a mindless thug, hell bent on realism. That's what the headline would have read - and thus the first seeds of doubt have been sown.

Within two hours we have convinced ourselves that no matter how arduous the journey the smart money is on us covering every known lie downstream for 1.5 miles. Lamont and I have had a continuous binary dialogue, crunched the numbers, worked out how fast the polar ice caps are melting, the effect off shore wind farms have on migration and the only conclusion is to vamoose back through the wood. This may be a counterproductive method – especially when you throw in the parable of the stationary salmon angler who catches just as many, if not more than the bloke who jumps about like a flea in a fiddler's armpit. Most of us crave some form of movement, however slow, to help close the distance, add to the sense of involvement and to absorb the wandering mind.

So half way back through the wood Lamont now injects the bastard bumble bee of doubt into my head by asking why we have moved and speculates that while we canter back – a huge pod of fish will be just entering the pool we have just left. And so it goes...having fought off the urge to stay stranded in the revolving door of indecision – we stick to our guns to fish the rest of the beat.

Emerging from the wood we make our way to a very nice run along three hundred yards of steep overgrown bank – getting to the river is a leap of faith through the Himalayan balsam, as the bank is a twenty foot drop down about 55 degrees – I tend to lead with my right foot, mine sweeper style, hoping that there is something solid underfoot. Once you're in the water you are tight up to the bank but with a single Spey you can cast in comfort. This is where Lamont and I part company as he slopes off to the bottom run and I fish through the pool enjoying a sweet taste of hope with each cast.

Minds like roulette wheels with a touch of Alice through the looking glass as we meet up two hours later with the time approaching two. Should we repeat the process or go upstream to another beat? Lamont is elongated in the long grass at the head of the bottom run when I find him. I have come to find him as I crave solidarity and to reaffirm my own broken thoughts and theories. Salmon anglers always end up flocking – no matter how fleetingly, just so they can share opinions in the search for any kind of successful formula. It's usual at this stage just to lie on our backs and stare at the sky, listen to the river, recharge and revel in our dumb luck. Maybe even have a smoke – the rest of the world in spin cycle – while we have gracefully managed to briefly stop time.

I think I will leave this chapter there – staring at the wide gentle sky, happy and still no wiser.

Chapter 9

Agnotology or bust

We don't really know

Isn't that a refreshing thing to hear given the age we live in? It's seen as a sign of weakness that could be pounced upon – Je ne Sais pas – I don't know. Say it too many times and life starts to get a little rough, so it's natural to have a swat at some answer and hope that the response is favourable. It's a world of giddy speculation out there that sometimes mutates into mainstream opinion based facts – two million years of self-preserving self-centred Chinese whispers began when Homo erectus bullshitted himself all the way across the African plains.

On a recent encounter with a real life scientist I came to realise that most of my bankside philosophy was nothing more than automated conversational shop babble with about as much meaning as a horse in a suit. Indeed in an average conversation the machine gun approach of firing enough clichés to eventually hit the target can overcome most situations of ignorance, but not with a dedicated full-time scientist.

Whilst generously volunteering for a couple of days for the Ribble Trust, I thought I would be able to prove a couple of my own theories with an actual scientist and in turn, unearth some helpful science based information that could be applied to my own fishing activities. The trust was conducting some electro fishing surveys on the catchment. In my mind I would be electrocuting a main pool on the Ribble like a comic book superhero and finally seeing every stunned salmon in a pool. Lifting the lid off the life aquatic - I would know all the lies and be privy to exclusive guest list knowledge. It was, and remains, a glorious wide-eyed mental image.

Observation, experimentation and reasoned thought – these are the foundations of scientific endeavour. I had seen an exotic example of a nineteen fifties aquatic survey conducted by the great Jacques Cousteau in his pioneering film – Le Monde Du Silence. Cousteau preferred the cunning scientific approach of placing dynamite charges into a coral reef and then blowing the shit out of it from the comfort and safety of the beach, then scientifically totalling the body count and then categorising the corpses. Later we see the French crew of the Calypso, soaked in island sunshine playfully using the Galapagos island's giant tortoises as picnic chairs, enjoying a glass of mandatory wine while chain smoking and casually chatting. Tanned and relaxed, these men were the best bunch of scientists I had ever seen.

Naturally I was slightly disappointed when I arrived at the Ribble Rivers Trust HQ to find that they had no dynamite, no wine, no cigarettes, no red hats, and only chairs to sit on. Nobody had a guitar or a hand gun, not even a sniff of a harpoon or spear guns. Fifty years was obviously a very long time in the science game. All this outfit had was a couple of buckets and a pick-up truck.

I blame Cousteau for making me turn up in shorts, flip flops, full of cheese, wine and chain smoking like Humphrey Bogart.

It's safe to say that these cats couldn't hold a candle to Cousteau and his crew. But I wouldn't let my initial disappointment cloud my experience. I would remain open minded and try to adopt what I considered a scientific approach, be on my best behaviour and more importantly try not to say anything stupid – which can be, at times of high excitement, difficult. I lasted about three minutes before the first dumb thing tumbled out of my mouth – "which part of the Ribble are we electrocuting?" thinking that we would be about to run out of fingers and toes as we counted stunned salmon. Gareth, the man of science in charge of today's show and tell, was clearly au fait with this kind of naïve question coming from a numpty volunteer with slender ulterior motives as he never even broke stride, continuing to load the equipment into the back of the pick-up as he quietly smiled and pissed on my day dream, "oh, we won't be doing the main river, it's too big – today we will be concentrating on some of the small becks around the catchment." Magic, no salmon to count and not even a tortoise to ride on.

Apparently we were conducting the survey to provide cumulative data on the health of the catchment, compare previous figures and then to highlight possible areas of need. I was part of a four man crew that included a trainee student scientist aged about 21 (who was already clearly more serious and mature than me) and another fisherman volunteer aged between 50 and 60 – it's a grey area, guessing age, not my strong suit at all – which sits in stark contrast to my self-certified amazing ability at guessing the weight of a fish. Lamont was always generously optimistic with his own poundage, which made everything an entertaining savage haggle to be agreed on before it went into his diary – once it went in there it became a stone cold unshakable fact. I had correctly guessed the weight of both my children when they were born – proudly nailing it exactly with my first born and being just grams out with my second while my poor wife rolled her eyes and failed to be impressed when I looked for acknowledgement of my subtle super powers.

We rumbled along to the first site which ended up having a water temp that was too high. I learnt that if the water temp is at the high end, around twenty two, then it would cause the fish too much stress so it's best to leave well alone and wait for the weather to cool. I had always wondered what happened to the fish during drought conditions but now I had a little more understanding – naturally when I talked about this issue amongst other anglers previously, I hadn't said that I didn't know.

Gareth was more than happy to explain the lengths that the Ribble Rivers Trust had gone to improve the nine hundred square miles of catchment. Analysing cumulative data and gathering new data to build an ever growing picture so they could implement changes and prioritise work. The removal of obstructions that impeded migration such as weirs and building fish passes were of paramount importance, as was the liaising with landowners and farmers to encourage better, cleaner practices. Couple these with habitat improvements and tree planting to create natural shaded areas providing cool cover during the summer months, and I began to realise what a massively important job it was that these people undertake. Some of the Ribble catchment goes through post industrial, built up, urban landscapes, and through clean up schemes and education in the classrooms they hoped to make the population aware of our incredible resource that needs vital nurturing.

By the time I got to our survey site on a small beck near the village of Chipping in the Ribble Valley, Gareth's casual informative pep talk had made me feel like David Attenborough – I was making a difference, I may not have been chained to the anchor of a Japanese whaling boat in the arctic ocean or super glued to a fracking well head, but I was now clearly a massive environmental.

It was supremely enjoyable setting up the survey site and conducting the survey. In a beck that I could have scrutinised all day long and still seen nothing, we quickly found that it was in fact teaming with life. On our first sweep through of the netted twenty five metre site we had plenty of Brown trout including some over a foot long. There where bullheads, salmon parr, eels, stone loaches all in impressive numbers. These fish were placed in small bins full of water with a pump attached to oxygenate the water. While the second sweep takes place, we measured, counted and recorded the fish we had and placed them in a second bin ready to be returned. With each sweep the count goes lower until we have run through the survey site a total of three times.

I have to say that seeing just a brief peephole into this microcosm gave me the shivers as I contemplated what a fearsome jungle it is, a world of endless violence – I nearly asked the scientists if fish suffered from paranoia (I think everything's trying to eat me) or persecution complexes. The constant energy sapping struggle for survival, living in this friendless danger zone would be akin to me being forced to wear a workplace electronic tag and my cracker factory desk being moved into the centre of the Human Recourses department. Danger lurked under every rock, in-between every tree root and every narrow hiding hole. Only the middle management large trout could consider themselves slightly ahead of the food chain game, but for them there were still numerous ways to buy the farm, usually it comes from above but remember the Otters' motto of - get fish or die trying. And all this incredible balance managed survival on a keen pollution free knife-edge.

How do you want it? – poisoned or eaten alive? I hate to be a pain and I know you're very busy but is there a third option.

Gareth was happy with the numbers as it provided a constructive and positive picture of a beck in rude health. We hadn't blown up a single thing, there had been no time to chain smoke and almost annoyingly for me Gareth had failed to look remotely like Richard Dreyfuss' character marine biologist Matt Hooper from the film Jaws. But even though the Ribble Rivers Trust must be held accountable for these obvious flaws, I can only shout with pride and gusto – Viva la Trust.

My selfless volunteer work aside it's time to embark on a 2013 season update – most of the Ribble anglers were having a stinking time due to one of our warmer summers that buried the river in sunshine and a few of the salmon with it. Mortality rates had increased due to the water temperatures rising causing a few fish to die prematurely, luckily the drought broke just as the outlook darkened giving the fish some welcome respite. Even then in early August the fish didn't show up. Right from the off the year was blamed as being "late" - theories as ingrained as the river bed flowed on several platforms of media painting a bleak picture. The grilse were late, the salmon were absent. Heads were scratched and bars were propped up in an attempt to answer our queries and disputes.

Was the harsh winter of 2009 to blame? Had the huge pieces of ice ripped out the reds? Could the barely sunk wind turbine cables off the West Coast be playing havoc with the Salmons' radar? The catchment brims with predators; seals, goosanders, cormorants, and otters were all the usual suspects in the frame for a lynch mob of salmon heretics. Had the nets men on the estuary had a field day? Could there be a nine year cycle when the Gulf Stream shifts taking food further out to sea, making the salmon reluctant to return? Could the catchment be under siege from poachers? Or was it simply a mixture of everything.

With the river on its arse for the best part of 14 weeks – how could the fish come? Would we have a massive late run in December? It felt like owning a central role in Waiting for Godot. All of us pinning hope on the species' seemingly incredible ability to manage themselves to maintain – to continue despite every obstacle in their path, *"of course they will come."*

Shortly after September a net was found hidden in a farm drain around the Balderstone area of the Ribble. The net was seven foot deep and could easily span the river. How long it had been there or more importantly how many times it was used is anybody's guess. If this net had been used at the right time it could have been devastatingly efficient. It was estimated that it was about a thousand pounds worth of kit. The shadowy owners of the net remain unknown – only they will know how much damage they did. One thing is clear, they certainly weren't playing at it. They were risking it for big money and they had meant business.

If anything, all these elements made us fish even harder in search of a pull, a sign of arrival to brighten the tone in our small world. We took fun anyway we could, finding it in unexpected spontaneous actions that just seemed the right way to think. A quick example would be the trail of shrimps I laid around the bailiff's car. Arriving an hour earlier and hell bent on finding a member of the club who he suspected of shrimping on our water – which was contrary to the clubs rules, our robust and larger than life bailiff had declared to Lamont and I that he was going to *"catch the cunt"* red handed. We wished him well and waved him off as he slunk off down the beat. It was too much to resist – never, ever look a gift horse in the mouth. I had some shrimp in the car from an early morning jaunt to a pool that I was allowed to shrimp. After a 3 – 4 year wait to get into a club there is little point in mugging yourself by flaunting the rules and then getting binned out in shame, relegated to wander a desolate murky day ticket hinterland. So as our intrepid bailiff carried out his bankside enquiries, I laid a trial of shrimp all around the boot of his car, drizzling them onto the bumper, even managing to place one decapitated tightly under the lip of the boot.

We shot off to the pub to await our payoff – it couldn't have gone better. He had quizzed a number of anglers who were on their way off the beat after another blissful days Ribble graft. They had told him that they were the last ones on, so he joined them back to the car park. Shot by both sides as the anglers get animated and start to stare and shout in unison, while pointing at the shrimp-mobile

– "who's car's that?!"

Meanwhile, up at the pub we were each led along the two benches of a picnic table in the beer garden enjoying a pint of Wainwrights and discussing the possible car park scene.

On the table my mobile phone ring tone chimes a door bell – *ding dong* to signify an incoming message.

The text read: *Where are you? You pair of cunts.*

So eloquent, so well timed – it was just a beautiful moment. Beer spat, Lamont and I had very nearly passed out laughing. The bailiff came and joined us for a pint and he duly agreed that it had been a perfect carve up.

The season marched relentlessly on without a fin from either me or Lamont to report. A very few fish had been reported that had been caught on the shrimp in low water but even when the river had lifted the fish still remained elusive. Fishing effort began to drift aimlessly like the river at summer level – there seemed to be a morose funk gripping the river as hope gradually faded and the worry was that the season would drain away. This doesn't mean that the river becomes a redundant or dull place. Each decent amount of rainfall reignited a dormant urge and intensified the thought process that this must be THE lift when a large number of fish enter and move up the system, doomsday apocalyptic theories are soon forgotten when hope floats and optimism becomes tidal.

On a recent lift we had covered our usual spots and landed again at our favourite top pool peg. As we surfaced through the undergrowth it became clear we had a visitor – Ahab had heard about our spot and had run the gauntlet of the wood. When he saw us it was evident that he was relieved to see us and was in some distress. He had been driven by the exaggerated jungle drums that had eulogised this pool. He and his hips and knees had managed to get up there but the consequences of the terrain had led to an epic failure when he had tried to get back. Yes when Ahab had seen his consultant who surely must have explained that Ahab should take it easy for a while and give the white whale obsession a rest – he could not have known what kind of animal he was dealing with. Ahab didn't care that his hips were as firm as a digestive biscuit – he wasn't about to let surgery deprive him of his passion for angling.

He was sat on his backside down at the bottom of a steep overgrown bank, his rod lay to the side and his bag was acting as a back support. "I can't get up - thank fuck you two have turned up, I heard this pool was good but the walk nearly killed me." Lamont's first question to this man in distress was in fairness to him actually what I was thinking – "who told you it was good?" I think Lamont didn't know whether to help him or take him hostage. I hadn't read about any fishing related hostage incidents and it wasn't covered by our club rule books, it remained a grey area but I was sure we would be at the very least frowned upon by our committee. Lamont looked at me for support, so I stepped in with a more humanistic approach for a man in discomfort. I asked him, "Are you a member mate?" Lamont purses his lips, raises an eyebrow and gives me an approving knowing nod that implies my worldly wisdom. Poor Ahab stressfully fumbles for his membership stored deep within his back support bag. Ironically his membership is produced from a much worn shrimp dye pink National Health Service plastic sealable medication bag, this verifies his membership status and we gladly help him to his feet. I myself feel a slight pang that his membership doesn't state: Captain Ahab – It does however confirm to me that he is one of maybe five rods that could be termed a genuine Ribble legend. I'm not going to name him, this book isn't about that – all that needs to be said is that if you think you're a legend, then you're not – that description is a definition for others to produce and promote.

Lamont and I get him up the bank and up to the bench. He sits down and it's obvious he is relieved that he has been rescued. Ahab then goes on to berate the surgical expertise that was supposedly meant to repair his hip. There is an element of bitter nostalgia when he compares his plight with that of eight time major winner golfer Tom Watson. "Did you see Watson get around Turnberry in 2009? He had his hip done and he nearly fuckin ran round, I have mine done and the surgeon advised me to give up fishing, bollocks to that!... Anyway where are the lies in this pool?" Ahabs right arm is outstretched and he points a shaky finger at various spots on the pool and we gladly fill him in on the places to cover. In return Lamont and I are entertained with stories and information stretching back over fifty years on the Ribble. This particular afternoon has become about much more than fishing, as we listen intently in open mouthed wonder to his unbridled passion for angling, freedom and slipping orthopaedic surgical standards.

Lamont carries his tackle and he puts his arm around my shoulders as we make our way back through the

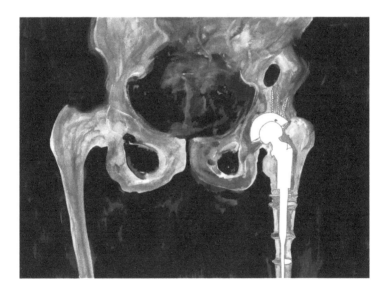

twisted wood. Ahab smiles and shakes his head - "I was just like you two…enjoy it while you can." It's quite affirming to hear that what you are doing is clearly right and to have it confirmed by someone who would gladly have his time again and change very little. As we lurch slowly with our fallen comrade back to the car park he continues to explain the pros and cons of nearly every beat on the river from Grindleton down, while also taking the odd breath to call us bonkers taking this journey with any kind of frequency. Obviously this compliment made us even more proud.

Back on the hard standing car park Lamont has the confidence to give Ahab his own homebrewed half-cocked psychological test. He asks this grizzled Lancastrian veteran who he prefers between Sooty & Sweep. It's an arc that I hadn't even mind mapped. Ahab looked mildly confused but focused as he gradually slid down his car slowly fighting off his waders. A lot hinged on his response, the car park became momentarily silent. Mercifully, Ahab breathlessly barked sneeringly – "Sweep,......Sooty was a stiff," as he continued his wader battle trying not to dislocate his good hip as gravity got the better of him. We both nodded in agreement – that he had passed Lamont's tricky test with flying colours, now we shared an invisible bond, bound not only by our love of fishing and the river but by a cheeky grey squeaking dog puppet with a love of skiving, strings of sausages, short cuts, foam pies and water pistols.

I go over to say our goodbyes and make sure he is well enough to drive home. He was closing his boot on his array of well-worn tackle and he suddenly grabs my forearm sharply, squeezes and staring directly into my startled eyes he whispers, "It's slipping away." As quickly as I was captured he releases me and gets in his car, starts the engine and crawls off the car park with those words still hanging in the air. As he rolls past Lamont and I he maintains eye contact just to drive home his parting shot. Was he talking about the season or was the statement a prophesy, a broader metaphor about choices and time... Lamont thought the latter, our minds wandered and a cold front slipped down my spine.

Those words wandered around my head for days while I threw my bollocks at the clock whilst on duty at the cracker factory – *it's slipping away* – Jesus, that was all I needed, more evidence that my life was counting down. Maybe he just meant the season...Maybe I should find out who Tom Watson's illustrious surgeon was.

Chapter 10

Situation Nowhere

Ed is a portal - Akron/Family

The season had reached the turn and was headed for the finish line, but at least the rain had arrived and for the last five weeks of the season we could occasionally fish in the right kind of conditions. It had undoubtedly been a sub-crap season in terms of fish caught. I personally didn't know any anglers who had got close to double figures, many of these peoples' egos were now highly sensitive and as fragile as kittens. If the wrong kind of track came on in the car juxtaposed with any note of self indulgent seasonal analyses that scrutinised the holy ratio between time, effort and measurable success it could easily reduce a grown man to tears. I myself had welled up when returning home after an eight hour shift on perfect water without any comforting signs of life – when the car filled with Maria Callas singing Un Bel Di Vedremo from Puccini's Madame Butterfly. It would have been a pitiless and ugly scene for any unfortunate eyewitnesses to watch a frayed nerve of a man sobbing. They could even have heard the music and concluded that I had been so moved by the shear emotive power, the bewitching artistry and the genius of the composition that I had been deeply touched. Unfortunately that wasn't the case, Maria was the trigger but the cause was my own selfish one solitary fish in a season plight. Mix the right elements, apply a dash of poignant correct context and you can quickly create a river of self-pity bursting its banks with tears. It was nearly as bad as when Kenny Dalglish announced he was leaving Blackburn Rovers.

All you can do is put these experiences down to an ongoing holistic education that could be a portal to a wisdom that has a beneficial meaning. I don't even know what that last sentence means – read it again. I'm going to say that at the next cracker factory meeting – I shall remain quiet and pick my moment and say in a confident, considered, thoughtful tone, "well all you can do is put these experiences down to an ongoing holistic education that could be a portal to a wisdom that has a beneficial meaning." – I'll probably get promoted to chief cracker.

The rain fell everywhere and left the river in great nick when Lamont and I fished a tree framed run at the bottom of the river. We had arrived at two in the afternoon just as another two rods were calling it a day, throwing in the towel and crying no mas. It's around this time of year when the full strain of the season begins to be outwardly visible - salmon anglers start to look un-kept, disheveled and slightly unraveled, jowls and shoulders drooped; wrinkles queued for any remaining facial space. In some extreme cases ticks and involuntary twitches appeared. These blokes where clearly running on fumes, their depressed body language and facial expressions said it all; both shared a Largactil shuffle and empty-eyed fifty yard stare. One I only knew as Platoon – I had dubbed him that when three seasons previous I had been lurking upstream when a very large salmon had hit his Rapala, exploded onto the surface, ran thirty metres to the opposite bank and then charged back, jack-knifed and thrown his lure back at him like an unwanted engagement ring. Platoon, now clearly dazed and confused reeled in, turned to the bank and slowly sank to his knees arms aloft looking towards the sky for some form of guidance and then did a desperate kind of silent scream of "why". It was an amazing spectacle – I was instantly reminded of Willem Defoe in Platoon failing to make the chopper as he is fatally gunned down from behind. Obviously when I ambled along from my unseen vantage point after a long and troubling internal struggle deciding if it was appropriate to interrupt this man's private trauma - I tried to calm him down by excitingly saying that it was possibly the largest Ribble salmon I had ever seen.

On this Sunday in Late September 2013, Platoon and his comrade gave no clues as they were both obviously all fished out. They stopped and we swapped fishless tales of effort and endless hardship. As normal within this five minute timeframe we also peppered each other with a couple of former successes just to convince ourselves that we were all good fisherman. Lamont won this little exchange of throwing flowers at ourselves with his, "I had four in two hours here last year on my birthday." Once again he had used a lump hammer to crack an egg. He then said a saying that I had never heard before. Just as Platoon and his pal were moving off he said "what's the point in hitting a donkey with a carrot?"… Both men looked slightly more confused but nodded out of politeness and continued their shuffle back to the car park. I followed Lamont down to water's edge and the head of the run. I sat back in the grass as Lamont got in and started to single spey – I wouldn't get in until he was a good distance through the pool. As I poured myself a coffee and looked up at the sky I concluded that hitting a donkey with a carrot was indeed a pointless practice. I couldn't work out whether Lamont was an idiot or a genius, after all it's the thinnest of lines. The season had been very hard, that we all knew and now we had also learned that there was no point hitting a donkey with a carrot.

"I'm in!" Lamont's shout shelves my donkey carrot idiot genius dilemma – his reel sings as a fish steals away and his rod bends in joyful apprehension, the fish holds in mid current and Lamont holds smooth and firm. Then the salmon surges downstream in a twenty metre left hand ark, line ripping abrasive against the water, the fish rolls and the hook pulls free while Lamont screams – "tu me fait chier!" – and then swears in English a couple of times, closes his eyes, and shakes his head in insipid recognition of what just happened. You can wait a very long time between Ribble takes. Everybody loses fish now and again, the name of the game is to minimise these instances. In time the great tussles that you lose actually can become bitter sweet, glorious and essential experiences that lead to personal enrichment. Lamont had done nothing wrong but that was little consolation at this moment. I was intrigued by what seemed to be an involuntary reflex for Lamont to scream out in French. When he was only twenty one, Lamont had lived in Paris for six months working as a labourer on a building site and he had always described his language skills as both effective and colourful. I asked him what he had shouted at his point of loss – "tu me fait chier!" he said, "oh that's just some street slang I picked up, it means - you make me shit!" This strange turn in fortunes concreted Lamont's genius status in my mind. Nobody in the history of salmon fishing had ever said - you make me shit! - after losing a fish.

Recharged with hope we fished on until near darkness called us back to the car park. The river would hold steady for maybe one more day until it would need topping up again. Fish had been confirmed as lost and found as information flowed from various other beats that gave us a broader picture. This lift and the drop in temperature had livened up the river and our chances. The meat of the season was upon us and it was now or never (next year). A feeling of urgency returned and a palpable optimistic tension grew among our small community as time ebbed away from us. I had only one thing on my mind – wrestle the Salmon Weasel from Lamont's formidable gigantic paws.

This would require a massive dose of luck and an

earnest amount of vigour; this was no time to be risk averse as Lamont was also handy when it came to the art of subterfuge. The weasel took pride of place in a custom built fly tying, fishing workshop. Usually when somebody wins a trophy they clear a shelf for display purposes, Lamont on the other hand, had instantly begun construction on an internal super shed within the confines of his garage. It consisted of many pictures of him and fish, Salmon literature, copies of Trout and Salmon magazine (which he once described as receiving on prescription), empty bottles of single malt, his horrible clockwork fly vice, material draws, tool caddy, and nets on the wall with a horizontal rod rack which nicely cradled all his many rods. A large reclaimed window looked out at his garden and house so he could keep watch on his property. A comfortable captain's chair was positioned in front of his work bench with a shelf just above this – this is where the greatest prise in sport, the Salmon Weasel, stood on duty. Before he had won the weasel there was just a garage. Now there was a piscatorial multiplex. Middle age had seen a mighty perspective shift that had made us capable of envy for the ordinary and the simple. A simpering jealously had festered and grown inside me of Lamont's perfect indoor fishing habitat and I knew that removing the weasel from it would render his palace a hollow and derelict shell; as unappealing as a mouth full of rotten teeth. The weasel was the jewel in the crown and Lamont had already won it once with ease. He was formidable when cornered, which is exactly where he resided with just four weeks of the season remaining. It would be a nice tussle, fought in the right spirit.

Our other worlds of work, friendships and family chugged on unaware of where our true thoughts resided. My auto-pilot navigates me through all these duties every September and October. I can glide through the cracker factory smiling, waving, nodding, showing the appropriate facial expressions and body language while joining in with conversations ranging from relationship breakdowns, football results, family matters, workplace dramas, Olympic aspirations, economic burdens, financial crises, crap television shows, technology applications and engage in entertaining pointless banter. I suppose it's like being a Royal visiting some area of their realm that they normally wouldn't set foot in but they are expected to do their duty, look discerning, quote a bit of background knowledge, get some first names right and even act interested for ten minutes. It's all smoke and mirrors until I hear some key words of river or salmon and I switch on to whoever has uttered the magic code to snap me out of my automated coping trance.

An opportunity to fish arose midweek when the river started to drop and clean up after a good spell of rain gave the river a decent perk. The river would be good to fish for two days at least so I had to take a chance. I was rattling round the faithfully banal cracker factory slowly eroding with Ahab's menacing words on rotation in my mind, "it's slipping away," slowly engulfing my no good lazy frontal lobes with dementia.

Six thirty in the morning and I am looking at the various cameras and online gauges trying to work out if the river is fishable or just a chocolate mess. The height looks great but I can't get a read on the colour so I jump in the car and drive to the nearest bridge (there is something very comforting about standing on your toes and leaning over a bridge) and confirm that it is a bit coloured but the right side of fishable. Time to do the deed and ring in sick, "I won't be in today; I've been up all night with the night chills." What the fuck had I said into that answer machine? What the fuck is a night chill? All my cast iron symptoms and almost credible medical history up in flames by haplessly multitasking – talking to the cracker factory sickline, while reading the online weather forecast and tide times. I will never know what made me come up with the Edwardian self diagnosis of night chills, my only hope was to say I had been running a high temperature and that I was in a confused state when I had phoned in. Either way I had to move on and get going, the die was cast. I was free to fish, there would be no point deconstructing my own appalling inept thinking. That would be far too time consuming. I followed my normal routine of pretending to go to work by dropping the kids off at both their individual destinations of preschool breakfast club and nursery. Returned home and cheerily kissed my wife as she set off for work. She knew with relief that the end of the season was baring down on me and also shared my view of the precious work-life balance so often overlooked and dare I say forgotten about by some other busy self important earthlings. An artist friend of mine had once said to me when discussing the weighty topic of "life" that it was important to remember that it was, "all ridiculous and meaningless." At the time I was sceptical – but every now and then that philosophy fits hand in glove.

I arrived at the river upstream of Clitheroe and found only one other car on the car park. I assumed it would be a pensioner enjoying a fine retirement but you can never underestimate the creative verve of the fiendish self-employed – they always seem to have an uncanny knack to escape the rigours of work just when the conditions drop right. On this occasion it was the latter. A builder who didn't have time to give a quote but could always find time to fish on a falling river – it was his customers who I felt sorry for, those poor vulnerable people who relied on a semi reliable time served expert to solve their construction crises. If that crisis took place in autumn when the river had a foot on and was falling– you had better come up with some coping strategies.

Surely it's a fact that Monday to Friday when the conditions dictate, our river banks are stuffed to the gills with the self-employed. Forget the mythical threat of the shady eastern European – keep an eye out for the self-employed. I bet they outnumber shift workers and those claiming state pensions two to one. Yes, these *heroes of industry* can't help but lose a day's income to get to the river bank. Fair play to them, as The Beastie Boys would say – they've got the skills to pay the bills.

I had spoken to the luckless Lamont who was duty bound and mournfully glued to work with an unforgiving workload. He used words like - circumstance, components, elements and finished with the phrase "all out of kilter." His day was in the blender switched to the crushed dream setting. He summed up by sowing some doubt seeds that he hoped would germinate, take root and flower during the day by saying that the conditions were not perfect and that I had used a valuable sick day too soon – that I had jumped the gun. I quickly told him that his work ethic was a guiding light, a sentinel in a moral darkness for which we can all hope to aspire. He hung up after a short outburst of foul language.

Charged with added soul power I found myself happily walking on a farm track with my spinning rod resting on my shoulder, accompanied by Marc the builder, brother of Karl the heron. He was armed with thirty years of Ribble fishing experience and confidently he informed me that he would put me on fish. I hoped he was right.

We fished the beat from top to bottom very thoroughly but didn't see a fish. All we accounted for was a few brownies and a small sea trout. This took us to about three PM and we had a sit down and a brew. There was something about the day that kept us going; it was a classic autumn day, slightly overcast with clear, crisp freshness in the air. There is an open clarity about autumn that makes it my favourite season – we live in circles, we live in inescapable cycles – autumn delivers a friendly arm around our shoulders that the end is also the beginning. Even though we hadn't seen any fish it felt right – we ran though all the theories but there was no escaping the fundamentals that apart from a slight peaty single malt tinge to the river (my preferred state) the conditions were fairly perfect and what's more the month was right. The Ribble is a back end river. Good water in September should make you fish all day – you are always in with a decent half chance.

This turned out to be the case. At four PM and just as the heron Karl arrived and declared that "somebody will get one in the next hour" - I hooked and landed a seven pound grilse that had taken a crafty upstream cast, fifteen gram, black and red Spintec flying C. Marc was not in the least bit modest and informed me that his supreme water craft had been the difference. It was the only fish of the day but it meant the absolute weasel world to me. I had an ass full of noodles and caught a fish while I should have been working. That beautiful weasel could just be coming home, all thanks to a mysterious but enjoyable outbreak of the dreaded night chills.

Chapter 11

Just Loving You

Ruby Andrews

When I was seventeen I was stood outside a pub in Blackburn town centre desperately trying to look older than I was in order to get in and be cool. I was stood with friends and a pretty girl that I fancied but dare not make any form of advances. She was eighteen, super cool and brimmed with confidence. She asked me for a cigarette and I slowly took out my ten Bensons and offered her the pack. She looked me straight in the eyes and flipped the pack lid, took out two cigarettes and placed them both between her moist red lips, then lit the cigarettes and passed me one, smiling. Jesus, I nearly fainted.

That piece of nostalgia isn't just a meaningless amble down memory lane. It's a tangible comparison to the feelings of happiness that flowed through me when I was presented with the Salmon Weasel in the Bay Horse pub on October 31st 2013– it had been quite a day. I had lost a nice salmon third cast of the day and then landed one of about twelve pounds with the tenth. It went quiet after that and I called it a day around three so I could meet up with some other rods for a final day drink. Later I heard the news that a guy had caught a twenty one pound coloured cock fish on the fly an hour after I had left, just round the corner from where I had been. We all agreed that was one hell of a way to close the season. Lamont grinned widely as he handed over our prise, with the words, "well done; you slippery shit."

Unfortunately Lamont hadn't been able to fish but could make the pub after work. His season had been his worst for a long time. He had managed to register only a solitary fish in late October that was caught on a free weekend so it disqualified him from counting the fish towards the Weasel. My season tally was also pitiful – three Atlantic salmon in an entire season. But what counts is the journey, so much to celebrate and sweetest of all was that I was to be rewarded with the Salmon Weasel to adorn my book case – she would proudly look down on me through the winter months and remind me of the importance of humour, endeavour and occasionally flicking the V's at life.

Winter

The origins of superstition can be a strange, fuzzy business; walking under ladders, lucky jumpers, shirts, shoes on the kitchen table, running round a church thirteen times anti-clockwise at midnight to summon up the devil. Where they came from and why they still hold water can be a mystery – logic sent on vacation, steps out and leaves the room while your imagination completes its mental collage of cobbled half-facts and perceptions all adding up to an actual physical act of superstitious stupidity.

Some of these manifest themselves as common sense, i.e don't walk under a ladder because you could get rabies. If you leave shoes on the kitchen table there will be no room for the plates. If you wear a lucky jumper then you will catch an Atlantic Salmon. Yes, we must follow the signs sometimes and ignore the facts – they can be unpleasant. I consider myself a logical man, when I need an operation I won't be asking for a god's help, I will be screaming for a consultant surgeon and anaesthetist. However, given the right variables and just the right amount of awkward circumstance I have at one time or another taken part in all of the above erratic superstitious behaviour, including the running around a church at midnight bit. That was part of a scientific test to prove unequivocally that the devil didn't exist.

Yes, we had been drinking heavily and no, we didn't have lab coats on – but at the time Lamont and I both felt that it was the only way to have comprehensive evidence. We had been discussing the blues singer Robert Johnson who, famously, was rumoured to have sold his soul down at the crossroads in exchange for his guitar playing talent. We felt that the devil seemed to do this in American folk law quite often ('The Devil Went Down to Georgia' by The Charlie Daniels Band being another example of a terrible trade) but Beelzebub seemed to neglect the population of the UK. I particularly liked the idea of a neglectful Satan – lazy and apathetic. So we thought we needed to meet this bloke and ask him a

few things – that's when Lamont told me how we could summon him up.

Granted it was a new one on me – the anti-clockwise midnight church gig had thus far evaded my radar, but after leaving the lusher and with five minutes to spare before midnight we found ourselves outside Sacred Heart Church in Blackburn on a black and rainy night. We debated what we would swap for while we jogged round the large, imposing red brick building. Lamont felt that pace didn't matter but the number of circuits was paramount. Fortunately he advised that the occult favoured only two numbers 13 and 666. Six hundred and sixty six laps anti-clockwise round a church at midnight on a rainy September Friday night while fully loaded on various agreeable substances was utterly out of the question. Our coordination and counting skills would have failed us almost immediately. So we concluded that in order for Old Nick to ever get any trade it must be just the thirteen anti-clockwise laps. The anti-clockwise part seemed a bit pedantic and some would say consumer restrictive – if we had been the devil we would suggest much easier terms and conditions coupled with more convenient opening times.

What would we be prepared to swap our souls for – Lamont is a notorious haggler. Over the years I had been on the receiving end of many thin end of the wedge deals at the rubbing fat hands of Lamont – I would have sympathy for the devil if he engaged in a transaction with him. Would we put the fragile human condition at the forefront of our actions and trade on purely humanitarian grounds? Would we swap for a halt to climate change or for a breakthrough in medical science that would benefit the most vulnerable…? OR

Would we both unanimously punt for breaking the UK rod and line caught record for an Atlantic Salmon by catching a game changing 100lbr from the humble Ribble. Obviously it was a no brainer – if Satan wasn't a racist and decided to turn up on English shores we would toss a coin and one of us would give away what we didn't believe we owned in the first place in fair exchange for glory everlasting. (It's interesting to note that Lamont's second choice would be to win the Olympic 100 meters with a sub nine second run, aged forty, with the attached caveat that he test negative for soul tampering or any other banned substance). On completion of our thirteenth lap and with our hands clasped to our knees, bent double with exhaustion and slagging off the Catholic Church for building a church that size, we waited patiently for nearly a whole five minutes…

The record books don't lie – Miss Balantine still clings to the record and her grip is unfaltering. We concluded that the process was sound enough but maybe we should have done our business on Halloween. More probable though is that Satan is indeed a massive racist and hates the UK more than Jesus – Lamont reckons that it could be because of the North West's dour, damp climate.

A climate I feel personally responsible for. Some years ago I received an unusual item as gift that I immediately poured scorn on. The object was placed in the household abyss, under the stairs. Once secreted there like an anal suppository, it's gone and nobody's going in after it unless they're desperate...it becomes part of a growing fistula of clutter that makes a grown man wince and grimace at the very thought of extracting something of potential need. Indeed, it forces you to revaluate what's essential.

The object or artefact as I now prefer to call it was an authentic Navajo rain stick. It measures just over a foot long and is an enclosed hollow cylinder, made of pine from the sacred Sequoia tree and is inlaid with Navajo symbols. Inside the stick it is said to be filled with small dried beans and was only used in times of drought. The tribe would use the stick as a rhythmic instrument to summon up the rain clouds to feed the land.

For two years it remained lost under the stairs, a relic removed from a proud nation at one with nature and its seasons (I had seen new rain sticks on the internet but they were just useless pieces of tacky novelty crap bought buy drunk couch tourists looking for a piece of ethnic America) and there it stayed. Until, during a fiercely dry spell that had kept the Ribble chained to a lowly summer level during the back end of August 2001...desperate and running out of holidays, I took the plunge to extract my only hope and after a distressing struggle with all manner of forgotten garments that had also been cast into the pit; I emerged with the rain stick.

I gave the stick several shakes and said the sacred Navajo words, "come on you twat, fucking rain." After this ceremony I stuck the kettle on and placed the stick on top of the kitchen cupboards.

Within four hours the whole of Lancashire was under a thick blanket of cloud and an unexpected rain lifted the river by two feet. It was a genuine stone cold Navajo miracle – I got two days fishing in on the back of that lift. I now held power over the weather – who needs a barometric watch when I command the rain?

With great power comes great responsibility – this I knew, so over the next few years I honed my rain stick skills to find just the right amount of shake to summon up drizzle or just to keep the river topped up for a decent height. I only really used it out of pure necessity, after all it's a rare scenario that we need any more rain in my part of the world. With this in mind the stick migrated to the cellar only to be fished out in an emergency. The last time it had an official outing was to break last year's prolonged summer drought as again my holidays had ebbed away with only a shrimp for company. I had been squarely caught hunched over in the yard, using a feeding the geese motion with my stick firmly in hand by my wife who said, "oh don't make it rain, it's been a lovely summer." She had witnessed the power.

I say official outing because just after the New Year 2014, I found the sacred and precious Navajo authentic rain stick in the cellar led next to the washing machine. Inadvertently I had carelessly placed the stick on top of the washing machine, sat on a towel in a wicker basket. I retraced my steps and remembered moving it there 48hrs previous. How many times during those 48hrs that sacred and powerful rain maker went through the ultra-violent spin cycle I can only guess, shaking in an automated frenzy like an industrial paint mixer – with two young kids and a weekly full team football kit - that washer gets some real hammer. It's been raining for eight weeks now and the damage is a full blown national disaster rather than a few localised showers. All I can say is sorry and that I can assure you all, the rain stick has now been destroyed as I wasn't fit to handle its mighty meteorological power.

During the destruction of the stick I found out that the ancient and wise ingenious Navajo Indians favoured the use of cat litter as contents of their mystical rain stick and that the mighty Sequoia is made up of highly compacted cardboard.

Navajos 1

Terminal Chancer 0

It's January 31st 2014. The salmon season on the River Ribble starts tomorrow. It's been 91 days since the end of the season last year. Winter continues to dribble and cough past with me involved only slightly, a passenger passively observing, gently re-energising and reassessing. I believe winter is for resting. I am at one with my weasel, books, log burner, glass, vinyl and stereo.

The best thing I have read during the closed season is a narrow selection of Orvis catalogues. Dog coats, moose bottle openers, squirrel nut bowls and even a set of ladders for your fat dog to reluctantly and breathlessly trudge up and slump into the back of a ridiculously large car. Only for it to be taken for a walk it can't be arsed to go on because of the shame it feels as it's the only dog in the park with custom Orvis balaclava, matching mittens on and boot ladders. All this and amazing fishing holidays in opulent lodges that make my two bedroom Lancashire terrace look like a dead tramp's liver. Confident guides seemingly carved from Montana hardwood with pearly white match winning smiles, assuredly look across bays and mountain ranges, all bathed in the most beautiful sunlight. Even the animals in these photographs look cock-sure of themselves. If there's one thing I can't stand it's a childishly smug pet that has done better for itself than I have.

I only tentatively bought an Orvis jumper for thirty quid online...now Orvis HQ has got me down as a potential cash cow and is surmising I have just enough dispensable income or that I may just be drunk enough to buy a safari jacket for that difficult day in the office.

Of course the real problem is that I have found myself, even without strong drink and marijuana in my highly docile bloodstream...strangely attracted to some of the clothes. It's become another dirty shame. At one time I would have rather chewed my own foot off at the merest

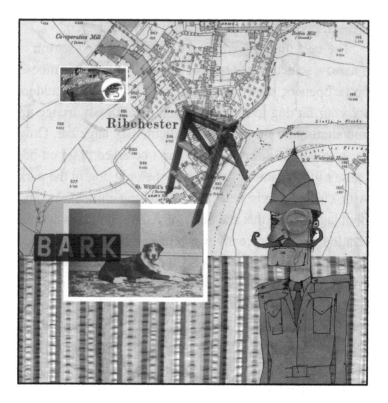

thought of putting on the Presidential Suede Blazer or the Cotswold Meadow Shirt but now in my mid forties this clothing catalogue capable of raising my pulse as I aspire to the glossy promise of comfort... Oh the honest truth of a cashmere sweater, the uncomplicated thrill of a pair of olive super cords. Yes I'm craving quiet comfort. I have to admit, the Zambezi jacket with numerous secret pockets for all those comforting unessential/essential items is a tempting prospect. It looks as though it's been hand stitched by a plague of oak aged weavers using only the finest exotically common cotton/nylon/wool blends.

I'm not sure where the appropriate place for the Zambezi jacket is. It's hardly what I'd call a day-to-day jacket. Surely nobody believes image is everything. Orvis say it's a travel jacket but to me it looks more like a trouble or at the very least an uncomfortable incident jacket ready for the perilous trip to a friend's house or a treacherous voyage to the local boozer or, on the other hand, maybe addressing Launda from the presidential balcony. Warning the cringing and crushed local populace that they had better stay indoors for their own safety and that it's on official 24 hour curfew until further notice. In one hand a case full of blood diamonds, in the other a golden revolver with monogrammed ivory handle. It's a very over confident coat jacket, it spews superiority. Looking through the small print I see that the Zambezi Safari Jacket comes with total diplomatic immunity a handy and convenient new identity, complete with new birth certificate, driving licence and matching passport. I may buy two, one for me and one for a faithful companion, Lamont, I hate to lamb it alone…after-all, you never know what steaming pile of putrid shit awaits for you around even the most placid bend in the stream.

Obviously if CEO of Orvis, Perk Perkins gets in touch with a massive sponsorship deal then my floating mercenary stance could be swayed comfortably into the patched elbow pads of the Zambezi as I drift around the local Poundscratcher.

It's time for me to wrap up the twenty thirteen season and throw myself into twenty fourteen. It will most probably be a classic silver season. The tiredness of last year's slim months have slowly faded away to make way for the ever elegant feeling of hope.

All that's left for me to do is gently lower the needle on to one of my favourite records – Ruby Andrews, 'Just Loving You', and listen as her voice soars away in this classic northern soul single. Close the laptop, reflect on the past, and celebrate the future and everything and everyone I love. I'm sure you've noticed by now that this isn't just a phase - its terminal.

The End - is the beginning